CONTENTS

CHEMISTRY
Lab Manual

Fourth Edition

Rachel Santopietro

bju **press**®

Greenville, South Carolina

The authors and the publisher have made every effort to ensure that the laboratory exercises in this publication are safe when conducted according to the instructions provided. We assume no responsibility for any injury or damage caused or sustained while performing activities in this book. Conventional and homeschool teachers, parents, and guardians should closely supervise students who perform the exercises in this manual. More specific safety information is contained in the CHEMISTRY Lab Manual Teacher's Edition, Fourth Edition, published by BJU Press. Therefore, it is highly recommended that the Teacher's Edition be used in conjunction with this manual.

NOTE: The fact that materials produced by other publishers may be referred to in this volume does not constitute an endorsement of the content or theological position of materials produced by such publishers. Any references and ancillary materials are listed as an aid to the student or the teacher and in an attempt to maintain the accepted academic standards of the publishing industry.

CHEMISTRY Lab Manual
Fourth Edition

Rachel Santopietro

Consultants
Verne Biddle, PhD
Robert E. Lee, PhD

Contributing Authors
Brad R. Batdorf, EdD
Verne Biddle, PhD
Donald Congdon, MA
Adelé Hensley

Bible Integration
Bryan Smith, PhD
Wes Barley, MDiv

Project Editor
Rick Vasso, MDiv

Concept and Page Design
Sarah Ensminger

Cover Design
Drew Fields

Page Layout
Peggy Hargis
Northstar Creative

Illustration
Amber Cheadle
John Cunningham
Sarah Ensminger

Permissions
Sylvia Gass
Brenda Hansen, MA
Lily Kielmeyer
Carrie Walker

Project Coordinator
Donald Simmons, MBA

Photo credits appear on page 214.

© 2015 BJU Press
Greenville, South Carolina 29609

First Edition © 1985, 1993 BJU Press
Second Edition © 2001 BJU Press
Third Edition © 2009 BJU Press
Originally published as *Laboratory Manual: Chemistry*

Printed in the United States of America

ISBN 978-1-60682-608-9

15 14 13 12 11 10 9 8 7 6 5 4 3

"ME, A CHEMIST?"

Yes, you!

"But I'm just a high-school chemistry student!"

But you can be a student chemist! Even if you don't see a science career in your future, you can develop skills this year to help you work like a chemist at your own level. You'll learn to think like a scientist—being safe in the lab, making predictions, collecting data, testing your ideas. Sometimes you'll have to think about how to solve a problem on your own, without any procedures spelled out in the lab. These labs will have the word *inquiring* in the subtitle. You'll learn how to tell when data that you collect is good and how to get it from the equipment you have to work with. This equipment can come in different shapes and sizes, both high-tech and low-tech. You'll use rulers, chemicals, laboratory burners, and good, old-fashioned glassware. But you'll also use the Internet, data acquisition technology, and maybe even your smartphone.

Welcome to the chemistry lab!

This book is your guide as you learn to use the tools and think the thoughts of a chemist. Be sure to check the Appendixes to learn the safety rules, equipment techniques, and technology of the Lab Manual. Read the procedures indicated by numbered bullets (❶, ❷, ❸, etc.) and follow them. Answer questions interspersed with the procedures. Measure carefully. Ask if you aren't sure what to do, or check your textbook for more information. Record data carefully in the tables and graphing areas provided at the end of a lab. And keep your mind engaged! You never know what you may discover when you do.

But what good is all of this? Why is it important to develop the skills and mindset of a chemist?

If you are a Christian, you're not just a student, or even a student chemist. A Christian should see science as an amazing tool to glorify God and help people by obeying God's command to wisely use His creation. We should do the work of chemistry within the context of a Christian worldview and use it as God intended, in ways that harmonize with His Word.

So . . . let's get into the lab!

Safety Icons

Pay close attention to these icons whenever you see them.

 Body protection
Chemicals, stains, or other materials could damage your skin or clothing. Wear a laboratory apron and/or gloves as directed by your teacher.

 Chemical fumes
Chemical fumes may present a danger. Use a chemical fume hood or make sure that the area is well ventilated.

 Electricity
An electrical device (hot plate, lamp, microscope) will be used. Use the device with care.

 Extreme temperature
Extremely hot or cold temperatures may cause skin damage. Use proper tools to handle laboratory equipment.

 Eye protection
There is a possible danger to the eyes from chemicals or other materials. Wear safety goggles.

 Fire
A heat source or open flame is to be used. Be careful to avoid skin burns and the ignition of combustible materials.

 Gas
Improper use of gas can result in burns, explosion, or suffocation. Be careful to check that the gas is turned off when you are finished.

 Poison
A substance in the investigation could be poisonous if ingested.

 Sharp objects
Use care in using equipment in this lab to avoid cuts from sharp instruments or broken glassware.

1   CHEMISTRY FOR LIFE

1A THE GREAT BISCUIT BAKE-OFF
Chemistry in the Kitchen

name_____

section_____   date_____

Egyptian sailors took them on sea voyages. Roman soldiers took them on marches. They fueled the British navy of Victorian times and the Confederate and Union soldiers alike during the Civil War. They were the food of sailors, soldiers, adventurers, and the common folk. We're talking about biscuits.

At one time, biscuits were the food of choice because they were light, nutritious, sustaining, and would keep for years if baked hard and stored dry. They could hold up under high temperatures and rough travel. Making biscuits relied on chemistry, and this is the chemistry that you will explore today. In fact, the study of chemistry may have begun with the science of food preparation.

Figure 1 Biscuits were the food of choice for sailors and soldiers.

You will try three different biscuit recipes in a great biscuit bake-off to see which one you like the best. When you scan the procedures and the list of ingredients, you'll see that all the recipes use similar ingredients and require baking at the same temperature for about the same length of time. But the small variations could make a big difference in the taste or texture of the biscuits.

Figure 2 Cooking is chemistry!

> **Objectives**
> ✓ Make scientific observations using all the senses!
> ✓ Relate the properties of foods to their ingredients.
> ✓ Explain how chemistry is related to the art of cooking.

> **Equipment**
> kitchen oven
> microwave oven
> aprons
> large bowls
> knives or pastry blender
> biscuit cutter
> rolling pin
> cookie sheets
> spatula
> flour
> sugar
> baking powder
> cream of tartar
> salt
> shortening
> butter
> egg
> milk
> toppings for your biscuits (optional)

Salt (sodium chloride) and sugar (sucrose) are chemicals that affect the taste of biscuits. Butter, milk, and shortening contain fats that affect their texture. Flour is the main ingredient; it binds the biscuit together and is what gives you energy when you enjoy one.

One of the most important ingredients in biscuits is the *leavening agent*, or the chemical in biscuits that makes them rise. In all three recipes, baking powder is the leavening agent. Baking powder is a mix of chemicals including sodium bicarbonate (baking soda) and some kind of acid or acid salt that chemically reacts to produce carbon dioxide gas, similar to the typical homemade volcano that uses vinegar and baking soda. Baking soda will cause food to taste bitter if there is too much of it in a baked good. Baking powder often includes other substances such as monocalcium sulfate and sodium aluminum sulfate. Eggs can also act as a leavening agent in baked goods when they are whipped. They also help combine the liquids in the recipe that wouldn't normally mix together, such as oil and milk.

Try your hand at some food science to see which combination of ingredients gives the best biscuit. Now, it's off to the lab . . . uh, I mean, kitchen!

PROCEDURE

Recipe 1: Basic Biscuits

2 cups flour

1 teaspoon sugar

1 tablespoon baking powder

1 teaspoon salt

8 tablespoons butter, cubed

3/4 cup milk

❶ Preheat the oven to 425°. In a large bowl, mix the flour, sugar, baking powder, and salt together.

❷ Using two knives or a pastry blender, cut the butter into the flour mixture until crumbly.

❸ Mix in milk until just moistened and turn onto a floured surface, kneading a little and rolling out to 3/4 inch thick. Cut with biscuit cutters or a cup.

❹ Place biscuits on a cookie sheet and bake for 10–12 minutes or until lightly browned.

Recipe 2: Baking Powder Biscuits

2 cups flour

2 tablespoons sugar

1 tablespoon baking powder

1/2 teaspoon cream of tartar

1/2 teaspoon salt

1/2 cup shortening

1 egg

2/3 cup milk

Figure 3 Culinary arts is an area of chemistry that affects you every day.

❶ Preheat the oven to 425°. In a large bowl, mix the flour, sugar, baking powder, cream of tartar, and salt together.

❷ Using two knives or a pastry blender, cut the shortening into the flour mixture until crumbly.

❸ Mix in milk and egg until just moistened, and turn onto a floured surface, kneading a little and rolling out to 3/4 inch thick. Cut with biscuit cutters or a cup.

❹ Place biscuits on a cookie sheet and bake for 10–12 minutes or until lightly browned.

Recipe 3: Drop Biscuits

2 cups flour

1 tablespoon sugar

1 tablespoon baking powder

1/2 teaspoon cream of tartar

1/4 teaspoon salt

1/2 cup melted butter

1 cup milk

❶ Preheat the oven to 425°. In a large bowl, mix the flour, sugar, baking powder, cream of tartar, and salt together.

❷ Stir the melted butter and milk into the flour mixture until just moistened.

❸ Use a tablespoon to drop dollops of dough onto a cookie sheet. Bake for 10–12 minutes or until lightly browned.

1. How do you think the biscuits you made today differ from those used in historical times, as discussed in the introduction? You may need to do some research to answer this question.

   _____

   _____

   _____

2. Taste all three types of biscuits, either plain or with the same topping on each. Which one do you like the best? Explain why.

   _____

   _____

   _____

name _____

3. Compare the ingredients of all three recipes. What do you notice that is different?

_____

_____

_____

_____

4. Compare the texture of all three biscuits. Is there one that is different from the others? If so, what do you think caused the difference?

_____

_____

_____

_____

5. Cut apart a biscuit. Look at the holes in it. Where do you think the holes come from?

_____

_____

_____

The chemical reaction that occurs in the process of leavening follows:

$$NaAl(SO_4)_2\ (s) + 3NaHCO_3\ (s) \longrightarrow Al(OH)_3\ (s) + 2Na_2SO_4\ (s) + 3CO_2\ (g)$$

The first two chemicals—sodium aluminum sulfate and sodium bicarbonate—are found in baking powder.

6. What would happen if you added more baking soda (remember, this is sodium bicarbonate) to the biscuits without changing any other ingredients?

_____

_____

_____

7. What do you think would happen if you added more baking soda than the sodium aluminum sulfate could react with?

_____

_____

_____

Two of the three recipes include the ingredient cream of tartar, which is the chemical potassium bitartrate, or potassium hydrogen tartrate. It is used in addition to the baking powder in your recipes and acts in a way that is similar to the way sodium bicarbonate acts.

name _____

8. Look at the reaction below Question 5. If cream of tartar is an acid salt like baking soda, what is it reacting with to form carbon dioxide gas? Where is this chemical coming from?

_____

_____

_____

9. Suggest some other things that could affect the texture and taste of biscuits other than its ingredients.

_____

_____

_____

_____

10. Milk in these recipes adds moisture to the biscuits because of milk's high water content. If there were a fourth recipe that had no milk in it, what do you think the texture would be like? Besides milk or water, do you think there is another ingredient you could increase or decrease to account for the missing moisture?

_____

_____

_____

_____

11. One of your classmates is allergic to milk. How could you modify one of these recipes so that he can eat these biscuits?

_____

_____

_____

12. How does food science involve chemistry?

_____

_____

_____

_____

Want a Second Helping?

Interested in learning more about chemistry and culinary arts? Search online using the keywords *chemistry in the kitchen*.

1B THE SERIAL SAFETY SAGA
Thinking Safe in the Chemistry Lab

name _____

section _____   date _____

Explosions! Fire! Flashes of color! These are what you want to see in the chemistry lab. But, actually, these are the kinds of things we *don't* want to happen in an uncontrolled way. Your teacher, administrator, and parents want you to explore chemistry safely.

But safety is no fun, right? Wrong!!! Getting hurt is no fun. In this lab, you'll have some fun learning to think safely. The table below shows safety equipment often used in chemistry laboratories. Be sure that you can find each piece of safety equipment in Table 1 in your laboratory.

Figure 1 Safe chemistry is fun. Getting hurt is *not* fun!

Objectives
✓ Treat injuries in the chemistry lab.
✓ Identify unsafe behavior in the chemistry lab.
✓ Locate safety equipment in the chemistry lab.
✓ Describe safe behavior in the chemistry lab.
✓ Identify GHS safety labels.

Equipment
digital camera, smartphone, or camcorder
safety equipment in the lab
MSDS or SDS

You will be taking some pictures and/or creating some videos to teach the other students in your class safe behavior in lab with a "Chemistry Serial Safety Saga." To help you know what to do, see Appendix A on Laboratory Safety and First-Aid Rules and Appendix C on Laboratory Techniques to give you some hints on how to create your videos.

PROCEDURE

The Safety Serial

Create videos or take pictures that teach your classmates the 10 safe laboratory skills and behaviors below. Be sure to answer the questions! If you demonstrate safety equipment in your video or pictures, don't actually activate them; just pretend to. Remember to look in Appendixes A and C to get the information you need to do a good job. Have fun!

❶ What should I wear in the lab?

❷ How should I smell chemicals?

❸ How should I mix acid and water?

❹ What are some examples of unsafe behavior in the lab? (Remember to make this video or picture in a safe way!)

❺ What should I do if I break glassware?

❻ How should I treat minor heat burns in the lab?

❼ What should I do if I spill a chemical on my skin?

❽ What should I do if I get a chemical in my eye?

❾ What should I do if there is an accidental fire in the lab?

❿ What should I do if my clothes catch on fire in the lab?

Table 1	
Equipment	Purpose
eyewash station	removes chemicals that may splash into the eyes
shower	removes chemicals that may splash onto clothing; also, may be used to extinguish clothing fires
fire blanket	extinguishes clothing fires; extinguishes fires on the lab bench
fire extinguisher	extinguishes fires in the lab (different types of extinguishers for different kinds of fires)
first aid kit	provides basic medical supplies for treating common injuries

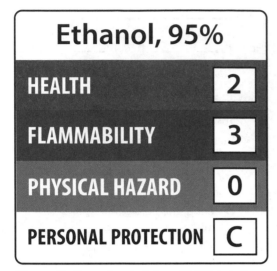

Ethanol, 95%	
HEALTH	2
FLAMMABILITY	3
PHYSICAL HAZARD	0
PERSONAL PROTECTION	C

Figure 2 Many chemicals have HMIS labels like this one, though they are being replaced with GHS labels. Higher numbers mean greater risk, with 4 as the highest. The personal protection area is coded to communicate the safety clothing needed to handle this chemical.

Put a Label on It

Now that you have completed your safety saga, consider the labels below. They are some of the symbols used to communicate hazards with certain chemicals. The labels are part of a recently introduced system called the *Globally Harmonized System,* or the *GHS.* The idea is that they can communicate safety hazards to anyone, anytime, anywhere, even if someone can't read English. Try to determine what these labels mean. Your teacher will confirm your guesses later on.

1. _____

2. _____

3. _____

4. _____

5. _____

6. _____

MSDS/SDS   *name* _____

Now, look at the Material Safety Data Sheet (MSDS) or Safety Data Sheet (SDS) document that your teacher has given you. Laboratories keep these in a notebook so that people can easily consult them. They are also available in digital form. Answer the following questions about your MSDS.

7. Give the product name for the chemical whose MSDS you have.

   _____

8. List any synonyms for this substance (a maximum of three).

   _____

9. What is the percentage composition of this substance?

   _____

10. What are the potential effect(s) that this chemical will have for each of the following types of exposure?

    eye contact

    _____

    _____

    skin contact

    _____

    _____

    inhalation

    _____

    _____

    ingestion

    _____

    _____

11. What first aid is recommended for each kind of exposure?

    eye contact

    _____

    _____

    skin contact

    _____

    _____

    inhalation

    _____

    _____

ingestion

_____

_____

12. What personal protection is recommended?

_____

_____

13. Describe the chemical's physical properties in the following areas.
(Write *n/a* if no information is given.)

melting point

_____

boiling point

_____

solubility in water

_____

color

_____

14. Is your chemical stable?

_____

15. Is it designated as being incompatible with any specific substances?
If so, with what?

_____

I have read the Laboratory Safety and First-Aid Rules in Appendix A
and have located all the safety equipment in the laboratory.

Signature: _____

Date: _____

2   MATTER

2A NEEDLE IN A HAYSTACK
Physical Properties of Matter

Have you ever heard the expression, "It's like looking for a needle in a haystack"? That's exactly the kind of task chemists often face—the need to separate a mixture of substances. Some mixtures separate easily, but others can be maddeningly difficult.

In 1898, chemist-physicist Marie Curie was up against just such a challenge. She believed that two unknown radioactive elements lurked inside an ore called *uraninite*. Uraninite is a mixture of about 30 different substances, and the more abundant of the two unknown elements represents just 0.00001 percent of the total mass of the ore! The second element represents even less. Definitely a needle in a haystack!

Curie realized that she would have to take advantage of the various *chemical* and *physical properties* of the different component substances to separate the mixture. For example, some would dissolve in acids while others wouldn't. Two similar solids dissolved together in a liquid would form crystals at different temperatures. By using these and other laboratory processes, Curie got closer and closer to her needle. By 1902, after processing 1000 kg of ore with the help of her husband, Pierre, and an industrial chemical company, she had just 0.1 g of her new element—radium (Ra).

In this lab, you're going to do something along the same lines, although it won't take you four years! You're going to use the physical properties of two substances to separate them from a mixture. Let's tackle that haystack!

PROCEDURE

Preparing the Mixture

❶ Determine to the nearest 0.01 g the individual masses of the 150 mL beaker, the evaporating dish, and a piece of dry filter paper. Record your results in the appropriate rows of Table 1.

❷ Measure out between 1–2 g of sand and 1–2 g of table salt. The exact amounts are not critical. Place both substances in the 150 mL beaker and mix thoroughly.

❸ Determine to the nearest 0.01 g the combined mass of the beaker and the mixture that it now contains. Record your result in the appropriate row of Table 1.

1. Is it possible to separate this mixture by hand or by using a sieve or strainer? Explain.

_____

_____

_____

2. Identify physical properties of salt and sand that are significantly *different* and might be useful for separating the mixture.

_____

_____

Objectives

✓ Identify significant property differences between several kinds of matter.

✓ Use property differences to separate a mixture into its components.

Equipment

laboratory scale
laboratory burner and lighter
ring stand and ring
wire gauze
clay triangle
beaker, 250 mL
beaker, 150 mL
graduated cylinder, 10 mL
evaporating dish
watch glass, 150 mm (2)
filtering funnel
crucible tongs
filter paper
sand
table salt (NaCl)

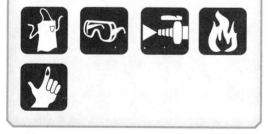

Refer to Appendix C on laboratory techniques for help in weighing and filtering substances and using a laboratory burner.

You will find data tables (when used in this Lab Manual) at the end of a lab.

Separating the Sand

❶ Fold and moisten a piece of filter paper as shown in Appendix C. Press it against the funnel wall.

❷ Set the funnel in the clay triangle as it rests on the ring stand's ring. Lower the ring until the tip of the funnel stem touches the inside rim of the evaporating dish as shown in Figure 1. (When the funnel stem touches another surface, it drains better.)

❸ Pour the mixture from the beaker into the filter paper. You may need to tap the beaker with a pen or pencil to dislodge any particles that adhere to the sides or bottom.

❹ Using the graduated cylinder, slowly pour four 5 mL portions of hot tap water over the mixture. The liquid (called the *filtrate*) will collect in the evaporating dish. Allow each 5 mL portion to run through the mixture before adding the next. Pour the final 5 mL of water around the upper edge of the filter paper.

Figure 1 Filtering setup

3. Is the water in the evaporating dish still plain water? Explain.

_____

_____

_____

4. Why do you think you used hot water for this step? Would you have expected different results if you had used cold water instead? Explain.

_____

_____

_____

5. Identify physical properties of salt and water that are significantly *different* and that might be useful for separating this new mixture. What about the water and sand mixture?

_____

_____

_____

_____

Separating the Salt

❶ Remove the funnel and the clay triangle and place the wire gauze on the ring in their place. Position the laboratory burner under the gauze, adjusting the ring's height as necessary.

❷ Place the evaporating dish containing the salt solution on the wire gauze, light the burner, and bring the liquid to a *gentle* boil. Allow the salt water to simmer until most of the water has been boiled off and crystals begin to appear in the dish. Do *not* heat so strongly that spattering occurs.

❸ Carefully pick up the hot dish with the crucible tongs. Place the 250 mL beaker on the wire gauze and set the evaporating dish on top of it as shown in Figure 2. Use this *air bath* to evaporate the solution to dryness. (The air bath reduces spattering and loss of crystals during the last stages of drying.)

❹ While you are waiting for the salt solution to evaporate, carefully spread the filter paper containing the sand onto a watch glass. Set the watch glass at the base of the burner. By the time your salt solution has evaporated, the sand and filter paper should also be dry. (If they are *not* dry by the time the solution has evaporated, leave them overnight and do step ❽ the next day.)

❺ When the evaporating dish appears to contain only dry salt (no hissing sound will be heard), cover it with a watch glass. Using the crucible tongs, remove the beaker and place the evaporating dish directly on the wire gauze.

Figure 2 An air bath

❻ Heat the evaporating dish gently to dry the outside and to ensure that the salt is dry. If no spattering occurs, heat it strongly for about five minutes to drive off any remaining moisture.

❼ Extinguish the burner and allow the dish and its contents to cool to room temperature on the wire gauze.

❽ Determine to the nearest 0.01 g the combined mass of the evaporating dish and the crystals that it contains. Record your result in the appropriate row of Table 1.

❾ When the sand and filter paper are dry, determine their combined mass to the nearest 0.01 g. Record your result in the appropriate row of Table 1.

6. Why did you have to take such care in evaporating the water from the salt/water mixture? Why not just heat the water vigorously until it all boiled away?

_____

_____

_____

7. What was the mass of the mixture before the separation?

_____

8. How much sand did you recover?

_____

9. How much salt did you recover?

_____

10. What percentage of the mixture was sand?

_____

11. What percentage of the mixture was salt?

_____

12. Do your two percentages add up to 100%? If not, explain possible reasons for this discrepancy.

_____

_____

_____

_____

13. Why was it necessary to find the mass of the beaker, evaporating dish, and filter paper at the beginning of the experiment?

_____

_____

> **Helpful Hint**
>
> To calculate the percentage that a component of a mixture represents, use the following formula:
>
> $$\text{percentage} = \frac{\text{component mass}}{\text{total mass}} \times 100\%$$

Table 1	
Beaker mass (g)	
Evaporating dish mass (g)	
Filter paper mass (g)	
Beaker and mixture mass (g)	
Evaporating dish and salt mass (g)	
Filter paper and sand mass (g)	

2B ZEBROIDS, WOLPHINS, AND LIGERS, OH MY!

Classifying Matter

name _____

section _____ date _____

Did you know that zebras and horses can produce offspring together? So can whales and dolphins, and tigers and lions. These animal hybrids definitely look different than either of their parents! People have learned how to breed animals and plants such as horses and wheat to increase their productivity and use for mankind—another fulfillment of the Creation Mandate given to Adam.

But the same is true for chemicals. Chemistry is the science of "breeding" chemicals, on the basis of their physical and chemical properties, to form substances which can be custom-made for specific purposes. Today we'll explore how two chemicals change when they come together to form a completely new substance with its own custom set of physical and chemical properties.

Objectives

✓ Classify mixtures and compounds on the basis of observed differences.
✓ Record and analyze your observations.

Equipment

laboratory burner and lighter
graduated cylinder, 10 mL
magnet
magnifying glass
spatula
test tubes (4)
test tube rack
weighing paper
sulfur (S) powder or granules
hydrochloric acid (HCl), 6 *M**
iron (Fe) filings
iron (II) sulfide (FeS)
iron and sulfur mixture

Corrosive: Avoid unprotected contact and do not breathe fumes.

Figure 1 A zebroid is the offspring of a zebra and another animal of the equine family, such as a horse or donkey. They are definitely different from either zebras or horses!

In this lab, you'll observe the differences in the properties of iron filings, sulfur powder, a mixture of iron filings and sulfur powder, and the compound iron (II) sulfide. You will observe and record their physical appearance. Then, in a series of tests you'll observe their magnetic behavior, their solubility in water, and their chemical activity, if any, including combustibility. Let's look at a match made in ... the laboratory!

PROCEDURE

You are going to be examining iron, sulfur, an iron-sulfur mixture, and the compound iron (II) sulfide for their appearance, magnetism, combustibility, and reactivity. Be sure to wear the safety clothing specified by your teacher.

Appearance

❶ Obtain pea-sized samples of iron, sulfur, the iron-sulfur mixture, and the compound iron (II) sulfide, and place them on separate pieces of weighing paper.

❷ Describe the physical appearance of each sample, noting any differences between them. Use a magnifying glass to aid your inspection. Record your observations in Table 1.

You've seen how matter can be classified either as a pure substance or as a mixture (Figure 2). *Pure substances* consist of only a single substance—an element or a compound—while *mixtures* are physical combinations of two or more substances.

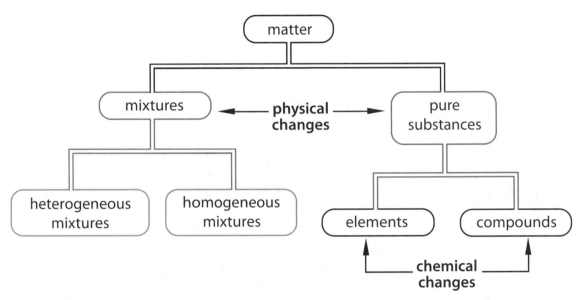

Figure 2 The classification of matter

1. From your magnified observation of physical appearance, determine whether the iron-sulfur mixture is homogeneous or heterogeneous. How can you tell?

   _____

   _____

   _____

   _____

2. Would you make the same observation for the compound iron (II) sulfide? Why or why not?

   _____

   _____

   _____

   _____

Magnetism

name _____

❶ Observe the magnetism of the substances by passing a magnet under each sample. *Keep the weighing paper between the samples and the magnet* so that magnetic substances will not stick to the magnet. Record your observations in Table 1.

3. What happened to the magnetic properties of iron and sulfur when they were combined in a mixture? What happened when they were chemically combined in FeS?

_____

_____

_____

_____

Combustibility

❶ Place approximately half of your iron sample on a spatula and insert it into the hottest part of the laboratory burner flame for about 30 seconds **under a fume hood**. Look for evidence that any of these materials burned. Record your observations in Table 1.

❷ If any substance remains after the combustion test, place it on a clean piece of paper and test it with a magnet. Record your observations in Table 1.

Reactivity

❶ Pour 10 mL of 6 *M* HCl into your graduated cylinder. Then divide it into nearly equal parts among the four test tubes.

❷ Drop the remainder of your iron sample into one test tube and observe whether a chemical change occurs (e.g., a color change occurs, a new substance forms, bubbles form). Repeat for the three other samples using a separate test tube for each. Record your observations in Table 1.

❸ Pour the remaining acid solutions (HCl) into the designated acid waste container.

4. How will you distinguish between a mixture and a compound?

_____

_____

_____

_____

_____

_____

Figure 3 Try to figure out which of the substances that you are testing for combustibility is shown in this photo.

5. How can an iron-sulfur mixture be separated into its elements? Can this method extract elements from FeS?

_____

_____

_____

6. Iron melts at 1538 °C and sulfur melts at 115 °C. Does this information help you determine the melting point of iron (II) sulfide? Why or why not?

_____

_____

_____

_____

	Elements		Mixture	Compound
Table 1				
	Fe	**S**	**Fe + S**	**FeS**
What does each sample look like?				
Did the sample exhibit magnetic behavior?				
Did the sample burn?				
If a residue remained, was it magnetic?				
Did the sample react with HCl?				

3 MEASURING AND CALCULATING

3A METRIC UNICORNS
Exploring the Metric System

name _____

section _____   date _____

Mutchkins, quires, therbligs, and virgates—these aren't fantastical creatures like ogres, fairies, and unicorns that inhabit some enchanted land. They're units of measurement! These strange-sounding units of measurement make us appreciate the standard that the SI system gives us for measuring anything, whether length, luminosity, or electric current. By using a common system, scientists all over the world can exchange information easily and without confusion.

Figure 1 A virgate was an early English unit of area equal to about 30 acres. It was held to be the amount of land a pair of oxen could plow in a year.

> **Objectives**
> ✓ Explore key measurement concepts using an unfamiliar non-SI unit.
> ✓ Relate metric prefixes when scaling up and scaling down base units.
> ✓ Determine conversion factors to convert from one unit to another.
> ✓ Convert from one unit to another using conversion factors.

> **Equipment**
> textbook
> roll of paper tape
> metric ruler
> meter stick

You've probably been measuring things since elementary school, but have you ever *really* thought about what lies behind measurement? Let's explore the subject by getting out of our comfort zone. We'll do this by inventing a brand-new measuring system and seeing what we discover.

PROCEDURE

All measurement units are based on a reference known as a *standard*. Some are physical objects, while others are phenomena created in the laboratory. To keep things easy, we'll use a physical object—your textbook—as a standard of length.

Working with the Unit

❶ Create a ruler with a length of one book by cutting a piece of paper tape to equal the length of your textbook's spine.

1. What is the relationship of your paper ruler to the standard?

_____

_____

2. Identify two objects in the room that could be measured approximately with your new ruler.

_____

_____

_____

3. What is a significant limitation of your ruler?

_____

_____

_____

Graduating the Ruler and Scaling Down

To make a measuring tool like a ruler more useful, it must be divided into fractions of a unit. This process is called *graduation*. The more graduations a ruler has, the more *precise* it becomes.

❶ Fold your ruler in half to find the middle. Unfold the ruler, draw a pencil line down the fold, and label it *5*. Label the left edge of the ruler *0* and the right edge *10*.

❷ Now, add four equally spaced lines to the left of the fold labeled *1*, *2*, *3*, and *4*. Then add four equally spaced lines to the right of the fold labeled *6*, *7*, *8*, and *9*. Use only your eyes to space the lines. Do the best you can!

❸ Finally, divide the first increment (between *0* and *1*) into ten small increments by drawing nine equally spaced tick marks along the edge of the paper.

4. Using the standard metric prefixes, what would you call the large divisions? the small ones?

_____

_____

5. What was the precision of the ruler before you graduated it? after you graduated it?

_____

_____

6. Using your improved ruler, measure the width of your hand and report your measurement to the nearest 0.01 book. If you'd like, you can come up with a symbol for your base unit of books.

_____

_____

Graduation

No, we're not talking about graduating from high school! Graduation is what makes a measuring tool useful. You'll find graduations everywhere in lab and in life: on graduated cylinders, thermometers, measuring cups, tire gauges, and even the controls on your oven at home.

7. Express your measurement to the same precision but using the two prefix-scaled units.

name _____

_____

_____

_____

8. What is a serious limitation to your improved ruler? Does a regular centimeter ruler have this limitation? Explain.

_____

_____

_____

_____

Scaling Up

We've measured things smaller than a book with your new unit. Now let's measure things much bigger than a book.

❶ Create a tape measure with a length of 10 books by cutting a piece of paper tape 10 times the length of your textbook's spine. Mark and number 1-book divisions on the tape.

9. Using a standard metric prefix, what is the name of this new unit of length?

_____

10. Using the tape measure, determine the length or width of your classroom and report it to the nearest 0.1 book.

_____

_____

11. Express your measurement to the same precision but using the prefix-scaled unit.

_____

_____

Converting Units

Sometimes it is necessary to convert one unit to another if you're working with two measuring systems. In order to perform this task, however, you need to know the relationship between the two units. A *conversion factor* expresses this relationship, either as a fraction or as an equation. For example, 1 m = 3.28 ft. Let's create a conversion factor for our book unit.

❶ Using the metric ruler, measure your 1-book ruler to the nearest 0.1 cm.

Ruler Skills

When measuring a length with any ruler, start with a convenient place in the middle of a ruler, such as at the 10 cm mark. The end of a ruler can get blunted with use, so using the middle of the ruler to start a measurement can give a more accurate result. Just remember to subtract this number from your final measurement!

12. Create a conversion factor that relates books to centimeters. Write your conversion factor either in fractional or equation form.

_____

13. Using your new conversion factor, convert the measurement of your hand in books to centimeters. Use the space in the margin to show your work.

_____

❷ Using the meter stick, measure your 1 dekabook tape measure to the nearest 0.01 m.

14. Create a conversion factor that relates dekabooks to meters. Write your conversion factor either in fractional or equation form.

_____

15. Using your new conversion factor, convert the measurement of your classroom in dekabooks to meters. Use the space in the margin to show your work.

_____

16. Using what you've learned from your textbook, state why your textbook is a good standard for measurement.

_____

_____

_____

_____

17. Again, using what you've learned from your textbook, state why your textbook is *not* a good standard for measurement.

_____

_____

_____

_____

18. Why do we generally avoid developing customized measuring units such as the one that you created in this lab?

_____

_____

_____

_____

_____

19. Discuss how standardized measuring systems are an example of good dominion that is pleasing to God.

name _____

_____

_____

_____

_____

_____

_____

_____

3B SILVER! WHERE?
Significant Digits in Measurement

name _____

section _____ date _____

Did you ever wonder where the coins in your pocket come from? You probably know that they are made at the U.S. Mint from different kinds of metals such as zinc, nickel, and copper. But it wasn't always this way.

In 1792, America was a baby nation struggling to get on its feet. The Mint Act was passed that year, establishing a standard of currency and a government entity, the U.S. Mint, to make it. The first coin made was the *half disme* (pronounced "dime"), or nickel. The thickness and weight of these coins were defined by law. The first nickels ever cast were made in a saw maker's basement from silver supplied by George Washington himself. Legend has it that the silver for these coins came from silverware at his Mount Vernon home.

Coins cost money to make, sometimes even more money than they are worth. The Civil War put an end to silver nickels, and the Mint eventually replaced them with the less-expensive mix of nickel (25%) and copper (75%) that we use today. During World War II, nickels were temporarily made of other metals since nickel was needed for wartime production. Making a consistent currency for a nation relies on—you guessed it—good measurement. Let's learn a bit more about measurement by taking a look at some nickels and seeing how the Mint measures up!

PROCEDURE

As you've already learned, measurement can be a complicated matter. While *accuracy* is one important facet of measuring, an equally important matter is *precision*. Precision has two aspects to it: it indicates how *consistent* repeated measurements are and how *exact* they will be. For example, a scale that reports mass to the nearest 0.1 g is less precise than one that can report to the nearest 0.01 g.

When scientists generate data, they need to communicate the precision of the instrument that they used to gather it. Instead of saying "I used a scale that can measure to a precision of 0.01 g," they rely on *significant digits* to communicate this information. And we'll see that significant digits also play other roles. Let's explore this idea in a little more detail.

Instrument Precision

1. Examine your ruler to determine its precision. In meters, what is the smallest *certain value* to which you can report a measurement? Explain.

_____

_____

Objectives

✓ Express the precision of laboratory instruments through significant digits.

✓ Use significant digits in calculations to maintain the precision of the original data.

✓ Use averaging to obtain typical values from multiple values of similar quantities.

✓ Perform calculations for percent difference and percent error while maintaining the correct number of significant digits.

Equipment

calculator
metric ruler
vernier caliper
nickels (11)

Figure 1 Compare a 1796 nickel with the nickels of today. Rising metal costs meant that in 2012 a nickel cost over 10¢ to make!

2. According to the rules of measurement discussed in your textbook, what is the maximum precision of your ruler? Explain.

_____

_____

_____

_____

❶ Measure the thickness of one nickel with the ruler. Don't line up the end of the ruler with the edge of the nickel; instead, use a convenient starting place somewhere in the middle of the ruler. Record your result in millimeters to the maximum precision of your ruler in Table 1.

3. Why is an ordinary ruler not the best tool for this particular measuring task?

_____

_____

_____

_____

Scientists and engineers performing precision measurements know that they must use measuring tools of sufficient precision or their results will be too *uncertain*. Let's use a higher-precision measuring device, a vernier caliper, to remeasure the same nickel.

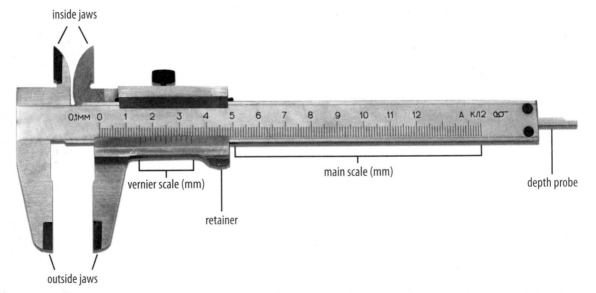

Figure 2 Use the outside jaws of your vernier caliper to find your nickel's thickness. Note also the main scale (mm), vernier scale (mm), and retainer.

❷ Using the vernier caliper, measure the thickness of the nickel. Record your answer in millimeters to the highest precision that the instrument supports. If you don't know how to read the caliper, ask your teacher for help. Also, be sure to clamp the nickel firmly but not tightly between the caliper jaws, making sure that it is flat. Record the thickness of your nickel in Table 1.

4. Compare the number of significant digits in the two measurements that you've made. What do they tell you about the instruments that generated them?

_____

_____

_____

Typical Values

In many situations scientists want to determine a *typical value* of something that varies from example to example. For instance, individual nickels vary in thickness due to wear and minor variations in the manufacturing process. There are a number of ways to determine a typical value, but the simplest one involves a mathematical technique that you've used many times before: *averaging* (or taking the *arithmetic mean*).

> ### More for your Money
> To learn more about the different types of nickels, search online using the keywords *types of nickel coins*.

❶ Use the ruler to measure a stack of 11 nickels. Express your result in millimeters to the maximum precision of the ruler. Record your measurement in Table 1.

5. Calculate the average thickness of a single nickel by dividing the measurement obtained in the previous step by 11. Record your result *without* rounding.

_____

6. Does your result have more decimal places than you obtained when you measured a single nickel with the ruler? If so, do more decimal places mean that your typical value has gained precision? Explain.

_____

_____

_____

_____

7. Round the result from the previous step using the rules in your textbook. Remember, the 11 that you divided into the measured value is a simple integer, so it has unlimited precision.

_____

8. What do we gain by averaging multiple measurements to obtain a typical value versus measuring a single sample?

_____

_____

_____

_____

_____

Evaluating Differences

Sometimes, it is helpful to compare several measurements to see how different they are. For example, how different is the typical value of a nickel's thickness compared to a single nickel's thickness? One way to compare these values is to calculate a *percent difference*. The formula for this calculation is shown below.

$$\text{Percent difference} = \frac{|\text{typical value} - \text{measured value}|}{\text{average of the two values}} \times 100\%$$

9. Calculate the percent difference between the typical value of the nickel that you determined and the thickness of the single nickel that you measured *with the ruler*. Use appropriate rules for handling SDs and rounding.

_____

10. Are you surprised at the result of your percent difference calculation? If your results are different than you expected, explain the reason for the final result.

_____

_____

_____

_____

_____

_____

Scientists also often compare their measured results to "official" values for certain quantities. These are known as *accepted values*. For example, according to the U.S. Mint, the accepted value for a modern nickel's thickness is 1.95 mm. To compare a measured value to an accepted value, we calculate a *percent error* using the formula below.

$$\text{Percent error} = \frac{|\text{accepted value} - \text{measured value}|}{\text{accepted value}} \times 100\%$$

11. Calculate the percent error between the U.S. Mint accepted value for the thickness of a nickel (1.95 mm) and the thickness of the single nickel that you measured *with the vernier caliper.* Use appropriate rules for handling SDs and rounding.

name _____

_____

12. Is your result consistent with what you would expect, based on your measuring technique? Explain.

_____

_____

_____

_____

_____

_____

Table 1	
Thickness of one nickel (ruler)	
Thickness of one nickel (caliper)	
Height of 11 stacked nickels	

4 ATOMIC STRUCTURE

4A NEWSY LIGHT
Energies of Electrons

name _____

section _____   date _____

News flash! Our solar system is not the only one out there. NASA has confirmed about 1800 other planets in the galaxy that are orbiting stars other than the sun. So how did we know they were exoplanets and not distant galaxies or stars?

Light from stars gives us information. Some of this light is visible, but some of it is in forms that we can't see, such as gamma rays, x-rays, microwaves, and radio waves. Visible light can tell us the elements that make up stars and the speed that stars are moving relative to Earth. Scientists usually find an exoplanet when it passes in front of a star, dimming the light for a short period of time. To get this information from a star, astronomers use a tool called a *spectroscope*. Although any form of electromagnetic radiation could theoretically be used in spectroscopy, scientists often work with visible light because it is easiest to observe.

Figure 1 An image of an exoplanet

Visible light, like other kinds of radiation in the electromagnetic spectrum, can be either emitted or absorbed by atoms when their electrons relax to a lower energy level or jump to a higher one. This means that scientists can distinguish two kinds of visible light spectra—emission spectra and absorption spectra. Emission spectra show the wavelengths of light that something puts out by showing lines of light on a black background. See page 84 of your textbook for a picture of an emission spectrum. Absorption spectra show the wavelengths of light that something absorbs by showing lines of black on the background of a continuous spectrum. Both absorption and emission spectra are line spectra.

In this lab, you'll learn just how newsy light can be. You'll get to observe the emission spectra of several salts using a simple diffraction

> ### Objectives
> ✓ Explain how elements can produce visible light.
> ✓ Perform a flame test of different compounds.
> ✓ Use a simple diffraction grating spectroscope to sketch a spectrum.
> ✓ Relate the color of light that an element emits to the shift of electrons into different energy levels.

> ### Equipment
> laboratory burner and lighter
> presoaked wooden splints
> watch glass, large
> spatula
> beaker, 50 mL or 100 mL
> colored pencils (optional)
> diffraction grating spectroscope
> incandescent light
> fluorescent light
> LED light
> chloride salts
> nitrate salts
>
>

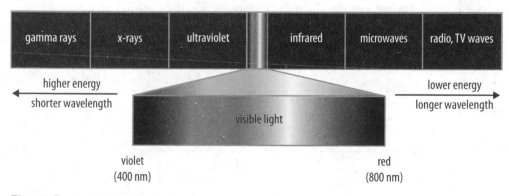

Figure 2 The electromagnetic spectrum

grating spectroscope. You will sketch these spectra and then use your sketches to reveal the secret identity of an unknown salt.

PROCEDURE

Learning about Spectra

Incandescent light bulbs produce light when electricity runs through a fine tungsten wire called a *filament*. This filament begins to glow, producing visible light, as electrons are excited by an increase in temperature and jump to higher energy levels. As electrons relax to lower energy levels, they release a variety of wavelengths.

❶ Observe the spectrum of an incandescent light by looking at it through your spectroscope. Note the calibration marks (400–800 nm) in the spectra below. Use your colored pencils to sketch it, or label the colors you observe. Add the letters ROYGBIV (representing red, orange, yellow, green, blue, indigo, and violet) at the appropriate locations.

In this lab, it's important that you have your laboratory burner adjusted properly. For tips, look at Appendix C, Using a Laboratory Burner.

400   500   600   700   800

Figure 3 Using a diffraction grating spectroscope

1. What kind of spectrum does an incandescent light bulb emit? What color is this kind of light?

_____

_____

Elements and Light

❶ Obtain samples of certain nitrate and chloride salts that your teacher has chosen.

❷ Fill a 50- or 100-mL beaker with water, and keep it close by.

❸ Light your laboratory burner. Adjust the burner until it produces a blue or colorless flame.

❹ The wooden splints you will be using have been soaked in water overnight. Dip a presoaked splint into each of the salt samples, and insert them into the hottest part of the flame of your laboratory burner one at a time (see Figure 4). Note the color change for each compound in the pairs before the wooden splint catches fire.

2. Name the pairs of salts that you tested, and describe the color that you observed in their flame test.

_____

_____

_____

_____

_____

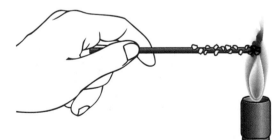

Figure 4 Technique for a flame test

⚠ **Fire!**
   If your wooden splint catches fire, simply douse it in the beaker of water you prepared in step ❷.

3. Which element in these compounds do you think is responsible for the color change? How can you tell?

name _____

_____

_____

_____

_____

_____

_____

4. What do you think is happening to the electrons in these atoms that causes them to emit visible light? Where do the colors come from?

_____

_____

_____

_____

_____

_____

_____

Elements and Spectra

❶ Now that you have found which element in these compounds is responsible for the color change in the flame test, obtain other chloride salts that your teacher has provided.

❷ Dip a presoaked splint and have your lab partner look through the spectroscope at the flame. Put the tip of the splint in the flame long enough for the salt to burn as you did before, noting its color before the wooden splint begins to burn.

❸ Have your lab partner observe the spectrum that forms. It will probably be different than when looking at an incandescent light bulb! Use the spectrum graphs on pages 37–38 to sketch the emission spectra of your flame tests. Either label or color the bright lines with colored pencils to identify them. Switch roles with your lab partner so that each of you observes the burning splints using the spectroscope. If you need to see a flame test again, use a fresh, presoaked splint and a fresh sample of salt.

❹ Repeat Steps ❶–❸ for the remaining known salts, using a new splint for each test.

5. How does a spectroscope help you identify elements in a flame test?

_____

_____

_____

_____

_____

6. What did you notice when you compared the color of the flame to the colors in the line spectra?

_____

_____

_____

_____

Mystery Salt

❶ Now, to solve a mystery! Your teacher will give you two unknown salts. Do a flame test of each salt, and sketch each emission spectrum on page 38.

7. What was the identity of the chloride salt Unknown 1?

_____

_____

8. What was the identity of the chloride salt Unknown 2?

_____

_____

Optional: Artificial Lights and Spectra

In this lab, you have been looking at emission spectra of different elements. These bright lines are emitted when atoms receive energy that causes one or more of the atom's valence electrons to jump from their original positions to higher-energy orbitals and almost immediately fall back to lower orbitals, producing visible light. The wavelengths (colors) of the light depend on the energy differences between the atom's various orbitals. As a result, atoms of each element generate characteristic lines of colors. You looked at the emission spectra of an incandescent bulb, which produced a continuous spectrum rather than lines.

LED (light-emitting diode) bulbs make light by the movement of electrons through *semiconductors*, materials that contain elements such as silicon and antimony. They don't have filaments like incandescent bulbs do. They produce light just like the elements in your flame test: the electrons are excited to higher energy levels and then relax to lower ones.

❶ Observe the emission spectrum of an LED bulb by looking at it with your spectroscope. Sketch the spectrum in the spectral graph on page 38.

name _____

Figure 5 LED bulbs

Fluorescent bulbs make light in a different way. They contain a gas that produces ultraviolet light when electricity excites electrons. The reason the electrons don't produce visible light is because the jump between energy levels is larger and releases more energy, and ultraviolet light has more energy than visible light. We can't see ultraviolet light, though, so the inside of the bulb is coated with phosphors. *Phosphors* are chemicals that glow when they are exposed to ultraviolet light, emitting visible light as their electrons are excited to higher energy levels and relax. So fluorescent bulbs convert electricity to visible light in a multi-step process.

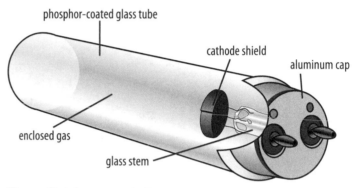

Figure 6 A fluorescent bulb

❷ Observe the emission spectrum of a fluorescent bulb by looking at it with your spectroscope. Sketch the spectrum in the spectral graph on page 38.

9. You may have noticed that the spectra of some artificial lights were different than those of the incandescent light. Compare both the color of the light and the spectra.

_____
_____
_____
_____

10. What type of lamp would produce the most pleasing light (i.e., so that different colored objects look the most natural)? Why?

_____
_____
_____

11. Can you think of any settings in which very good lighting is essential for work and productivity?

_____

_____

_____

12. Since each element produces a characteristic spectrum, what can you conclude about the location of the electrons?

_____

_____

13. Suppose that you had used the same wooden splint to burn all the salts in succession. What difficulty could this have introduced?

_____

_____

_____

14. Helium was discovered in the sun before it was discovered on the earth. How could this be?

_____

_____

_____

Look at the absorption spectrum from a star shown on the lower left. The black lines display wavelengths of light that are absorbed by the gases in the star.

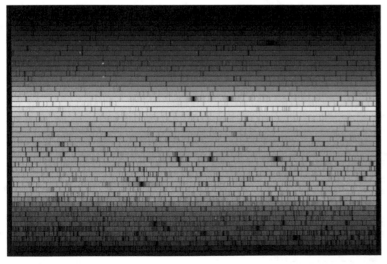

15. Why is this information useful?

_____

_____

16. If emission lines are created in a spectrum when an electron falls from an excited state to a relaxed state, how would you explain absorption lines?

_____

_____

_____

_____

SPECTRAL SKETCHES

name _____

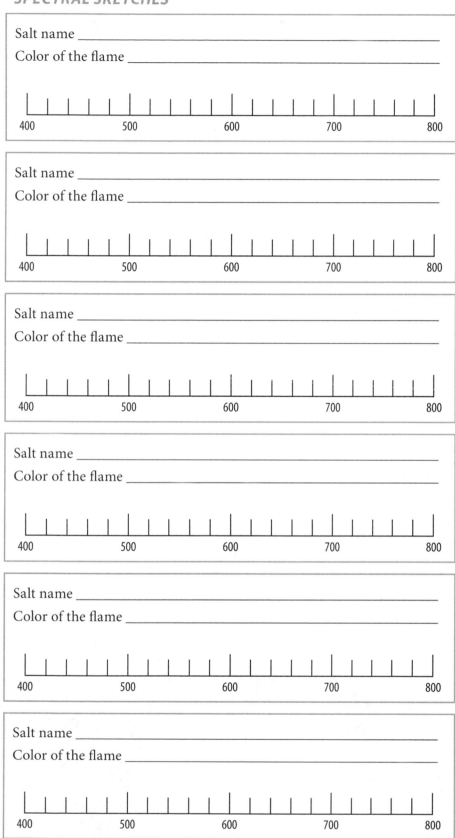

Salt name _____

Color of the flame _____

400   500   600   700   800

Salt name _____

Color of the flame _____

400   500   600   700   800

Salt name _____

Color of the flame _____

400   500   600   700   800

Salt name _____

Color of the flame _____

400   500   600   700   800

Salt name _____

Color of the flame _____

400   500   600   700   800

Salt name _____

Color of the flame _____

400   500   600   700   800

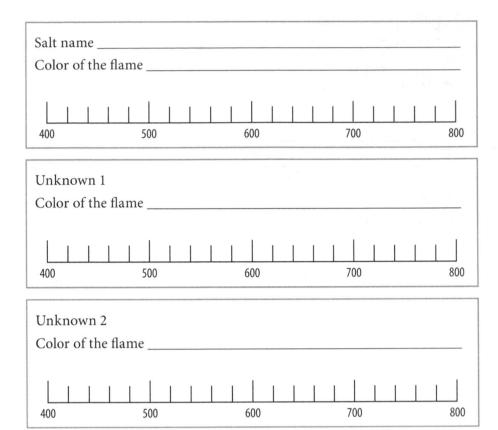

Salt name _____

Color of the flame _____

| | | | | | | | | | | | | | | | | | | | |
400   500   600   700   800

Unknown 1

Color of the flame _____

| | | | | | | | | | | | | | | | | | | | |
400   500   600   700   800

Unknown 2

Color of the flame _____

| | | | | | | | | | | | | | | | | | | | |
400   500   600   700   800

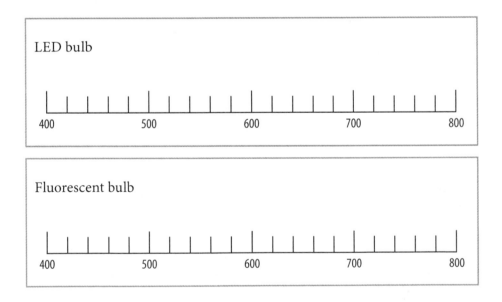

LED bulb

| | | | | | | | | | | | | | | | | | | | |
400   500   600   700   800

Fluorescent bulb

| | | | | | | | | | | | | | | | | | | | |
400   500   600   700   800

4B COPPER CROOKS
Mixtures of Isotopes

Burglars break into homes and businesses, tearing apart walls and fixtures. What are they looking for? Jewelry? Maybe. Electronics? Possibly. Often they are looking for copper, which is quite the valuable commodity these days! Crooks will tear out water pipes and even knock down lights on poles and telephone wires looking for copper pipes and copper wire. Some have even been electrocuted in the process!

Copper wire is made of pure copper, but this copper exists in two different but common and stable isotopes—copper-63 and copper-65. On the periodic table the atomic mass of copper is listed as 63.55. Why is this? Naturally occurring elements are usually mixtures of isotopes. This is why the atomic masses listed on the periodic table are not whole numbers. Instead, they are the weighted averages of the various isotopes of each element.

Figure 1 From the atomic mass on the periodic table, can you determine which isotope of copper is more common in copper wire?

You can calculate atomic mass by using the following formula:

$$\text{weighted average} = \frac{\text{total mass of atoms}}{\text{total number of atoms}}.$$

To determine the total mass, you must first determine how much mass each kind of atom (isotope) contributes. The formula for this calculation is shown below.

$$\text{total mass} = \overbrace{\text{mass of one atom}_1 \times \text{number of atoms}_1}^{\text{Isotope 1}} + \overbrace{\text{mass of one atom}_2 \times \text{number of atoms}_2}^{\text{Isotope 2}}.$$

In this experiment, you will use a mixture of two varieties of chocolate-covered candies to represent two different isotopes in 1 mol of the "element" ememium.

PROCEDURE

❶ Obtain a mixture of 50 candies from your teacher.

❷ Find the mass of five large candies and five small candies. Make sure you report one estimated digit if you are reading a triple beam balance.

1. Mass of five large candies in grams (m_l):

_____

2. Mass of five small candies in grams (m_s):

_____

Figure 2 The Statue of Liberty is green because pure copper reacts to form a green patina called *verdigris*.

❸ Divide each mass by 5 to get an average mass for each type of candy. Make sure you use SDs properly!

3. Average mass of one large candy in grams:

_____

4. Average mass of one small candy in grams:

_____

❹ Count the number of large candies and the number of small candies.

5. Number of large candies in the mixture (n_l):

_____

6. Number of small candies in the mixture (n_s):

_____

Now you will calculate the weighted average of the masses of candies in the mixture as instructed below. You can look at Example Problem 4-4 on page 103 of your textbook. Be sure to follow the significant digit rules. Show your work in the margin.

7. Without weighing them, calculate the total mass of your sample of candies according to the equation below.

$$m_{total} = (m_l \times n_l) + (m_s \times n_s)$$

_____

_____

Now calculate the weighted average of each candy piece using the formula below. This is similar to the atomic mass of elements that you find on the periodic table.

$$\text{weighted average} = \frac{m_{total}}{\text{total number of candies } (n_l + n_s)}$$

8. What is the weighted average of your candies?

_____

❺ Calculate the percentage of each "isotope" in the candy mixture. Using average masses, solve for the percentage of each type of candy ("isotope") according to the equation below. Substitute your calculated value for the weighted average and the masses from above; then solve for x and $(1 - x)$. Let x be the fraction that is m_l, and let $(1 - x)$ be the fraction that is m_s. Once you have values for x and $(1 - x)$, express each as a percent.

$$\text{weighted average} = (x - m_l) + [(1 - x) \times m_s]$$

9. What is the percentage of large candies and small candies that you calculated?

_____

Remember to follow the rules for significant digits when adding, multiplying, and dividing your weights.

Now verify your calculations from question 9, using the formulas below, where the actual numbers of candies ("isotopes") are used.

name _____

$$\% \text{ large candies } = \frac{n_l}{\text{total number}} \times 100$$

$$\% \text{ small candies } = \frac{n_s}{\text{total number}} \times 100$$

10. What is the percentage of large candies and small candies that you counted?

   _____

11. Account for any differences between the answers for Questions 9 and 10.

   _____

   _____

12. Explain why the atomic mass on the periodic table for copper is not a whole number. Which isotope is more common in natural copper?

   _____

   _____

   _____

   _____

Copper has 27 other isotopes, all of which are radioactive, or radio-isotopes. You'll learn more about radioisotopes in Chapter 20. These isotopes are unstable, short-lived, and relatively rare.

13. How would radioisotopes of copper affect the atomic mass of copper on the periodic table?

   _____

   _____

14. The radioisotopes of copper are very useful in medicine for making images of the body and for treating cancer. Where do you think scientists would get these radioisotopes?

   _____

   _____

15. How can the chemistry of copper be used to fulfill God's commands?

   _____

   _____

   _____

5 ELEMENTS

5 AN ELEMENTAL MERRY-GO-ROUND
Periodic Trends

name _____

section _____   date _____

Periodic tables are not one-size-fits-all. They can use spirals, steps, and even amoeba shapes to communicate information about how the characteristics of elements change with their atomic number. This idea is what you've come to know as the *periodic law.*

The periodic table is arranged so that all the elements that appear in similar positions in the cycle of properties are in the same vertical column in the table. For example, since Li, Na, K, Rb, Cs, and Fr appear at similar points in the cycle for atomic radii, they are placed in the same vertical column. Vertical columns are called *groups* or *families,* and horizontal rows are called *periods* or *series.* Properties vary according to a pattern as you move across a period or down a group.

So just how periodic is the periodic table? In this lab exercise, you will graph the atomic radii of elements from several periods and one group from the periodic table. You will then use these graphs to predict the atomic radii of other elements. You'll explore how atomic radii increase as you move across a period and down a group of the periodic table. Let's spin that merry-go-round!

Objectives

✓ Demonstrate periodic patterns by graphing atomic radii and their atomic numbers.

✓ Predict other atomic radii on the basis of periodic patterns.

✓ Relate the function and organization of the periodic table to the modeling nature of science.

Equipment
metric ruler

Figure 1 The main idea of this spiral periodic table is to show the periodic nature of the elements. Makes you think of a merry-go-round!

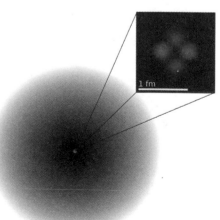

1 pm = 1000 fm

Figure 2 You can see that finding the radius of an atom is not so easy!

> ### *Element Superlatives*
>
> Figure 3 shows a periodic table with atomic radius information. Which atom is the largest? Which is the smallest? Can you use this information to predict the general trend of atomic radii?

PROCEDURE

❶ Using the data from the periodic table in Figure 3 on page 46, plot the atomic radius of each element in Periods 1–4. Plot the atomic number on the *x*-axis and the atomic radius on the *y*-axis on Graph 1 of the graphing area provided at the end of this lab.

❷ Using a ruler, connect each consecutive point with a straight line and label the major peaks on the graph with the symbol of the appropriate element.

1. Which elements occupy the peaks in the cycles on Graph 1?

   _____

2. Do the periods, or cycles, each contain the same number of elements in Graph 1?

   _____

3. Are there any areas of Graph 1 that seem to contradict the pattern?

   _____

   _____

4. Using Graph 1, predict the radii of Mg and Fe.

   _____

5. Compare your atomic radius values for Mg and Fe to the actual values obtained from your teacher. What is your percent error for each element? (Show your setups in the margin.)

   $$\text{Percent error} = \frac{\left|\text{actual value } - \text{ measured value}\right|}{\text{actual value}} \times 100\%$$

   _____

❸ Using the data in the periodic table, plot the atomic radius of each Group 1 element. Plot the atomic number on the *x*-axis and the atomic radius on the *y*-axis on Graph 2 of the graphing area provided at the end of this lab.

❹ Connect the data points with a smooth curve.

6. Consider the curve obtained in Graph 2. Is it in a form you would expect for elements within a group? Explain.

   _____

   _____

7. Using Graph 2, predict the atomic radius of Na.

   _____

8. Compare your atomic radius values for Na to the actual value obtained from your teacher. What is your percent error? (Show your setups in the margin.)

_____

_____

name _____

9. Would it be useful to organize the elements in an alphabetized table? Why or why not?

_____

_____

_____

_____

10. (Optional) Suggest another way that you could organize the periodic table.

_____

_____

_____

_____

11. How is the periodic table an example of a model in science? (See Chapter 1, pages 2–3, of your textbook.)

_____

_____

_____

_____

PERIODIC TABLE OF THE ELEMENTS WITH ATOMIC RADII

GROUP																	
1A																	8A
1 **H** 53	2A											3A	4A	5A	6A	7A	2 **He** 31
3 **Li** 167	4 **Be** 112											5 **B** 87	6 **C** 67	7 **N** 56	8 **O** 48	9 **F** 42	10 **Ne** 38
11 **Na**	12 **Mg**	3B	4B	5B	6B	7B		8B		1B	2B	13 **Al** 118	14 **Si** 111	15 **P** 98	16 **S** 88	17 **Cl** 79	18 **Ar** 71
19 **K** 243	20 **Ca** 194	21 **Sc** 184	22 **Ti** 176	23 **V** 171	24 **Cr** 166	25 **Mn** 161	26 **Fe**	27 **Co** 152	28 **Ni** 149	29 **Cu** 145	30 **Zn** 142	31 **Ga** 136	32 **Ge** 125	33 **As** 114	34 **Se** 103	35 **Br** 94	36 **Kr** 88
37 **Rb** 265	38 **Sr** 219	39 **Y** 212	40 **Zr** 206	41 **Nb** 198	42 **Mo** 190	43 **Tc** 183	44 **Ru** 178	45 **Rh** 173	46 **Pd** 169	47 **Ag** 165	48 **Cd** 161	49 **In** 156	50 **Sn** 145	51 **Sb** 133	52 **Te** 123	53 **I** 115	54 **Xe** 108
55 **Cs** 298	56 **Ba** 253	57 **La**	72 **Hf** 208	73 **Ta** 200	74 **W** 193	75 **Re** 188	76 **Os** 185	77 **Ir** 180	78 **Pt** 177	79 **Au** 174	80 **Hg** 171	81 **Tl** 156	82 **Pb** 154	83 **Bi** 143	84 **Po** 135	85 **At**	86 **Rn** 120
87 **Fr**	88 **Ra**	89 **Ac**	104 **Rf**	105 **Db**	106 **Sg**	107 **Bh**	108 **Hs**	109 **Mt**	110 **Ds**	111 **Rg**	112 **Cn**	113 **Uut**	114 **Fl**	115 **Uup**	116 **Lv**	117 **Uus**	118 **Uuo**

58 **Ce**	59 **Pr** 247	60 **Nd** 206	61 **Pm** 205	62 **Sm** 238	63 **Eu** 231	64 **Gd** 233	65 **Tb** 225	66 **Dy** 228	67 **Ho**	68 **Er** 226	69 **Tm** 222	70 **Yb** 222	71 **Lu** 217
90 **Th**	91 **Pa**	92 **U**	93 **Np**	94 **Pu**	95 **Am**	96 **Cm**	97 **Bk**	98 **Cf**	99 **Es**	100 **Fm**	101 **Md**	102 **No**	103 **Lr**

Figure 3   Periodic table with calculated atomic radii (in red) in picometers

name _____

Graph 1

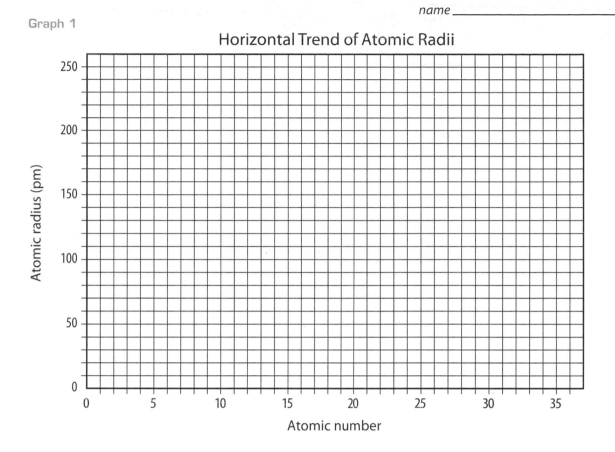

Graph 2

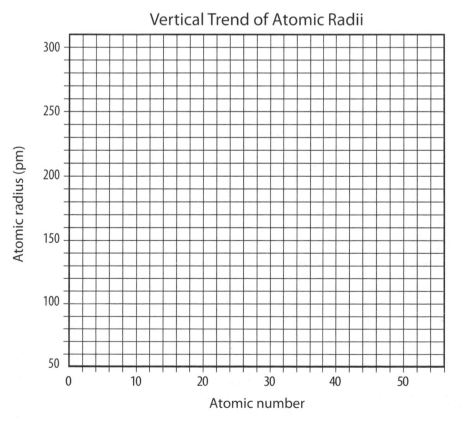

6   CHEMICAL BONDS

6 BULLETPROOF CHEMISTRY
Chemical Bonds and Physical Properties

A woman approached a teller one April morning in 2012 at a BB&T bank in Smyrna, Georgia. In the slot under the wall of glass, she passed to the attendant a typed demand note. When the teller moved too slowly, she pulled a gun and demanded money. Happily, the glass was bulletproof. Eventually, the would-be bank robber left without a dime, foiled by chemistry!

Figure 1 Bulletproof glass is made by putting together two different types of glass. Both are transparent, but one is more flexible than the other. Glass is made mostly of silicon dioxide, a covalent compound with the same formula as sand.

Chemical bonds are responsible for the physical properties of substances such as bulletproof glass. We can use these properties to keep our homes warm, cook our food, and make great running shoes. You'll learn more about materials chemistry in Chapter 19.

Ionic, covalent, and metallic bonds play a big role in determining the physical properties of substances. If you can observe the physical properties of a substance, you can often determine its bond type. In the table on the next page, notice the properties that each bond type typically produces in substances.

name _____

section _____   date _____

Objectives

- ✓ Relate physical properties of compounds to their chemical properties.
- ✓ Investigate the melting points of ionic, covalent, and metallic substances.
- ✓ Investigate the solubility and conductivity of ionic, covalent, and metallic bonds.
- ✓ Experiment to identify unknown substances using a variety of tests.

Equipment

laboratory scale (accurate to 0.1 g)
laboratory burner and lighter
conductivity tester
evaporating dish
ring stand and ring
test tubes (6)
test tube rack
weighing paper
wire gauze
masking tape
acetone
unknown substances (3)

		Bond Type		
		Ionic bond	**Covalent bond**	**Metallic bond**
Characteristics	**Electrons**	transferred	shared	free
	Smallest unit	formula unit	molecule	atom
	Melting point	forms solids with high melting points	forms solids (with low melting points), liquids, and gases	forms solids with relatively high melting points
	Solubility	often soluble in water but insoluble in organic solvents	usually insoluble in water but soluble in organic solvents	insoluble in both water and organic solvents
	Conductivity	conducts electricity when melted or dissolved	usually does not conduct electricity	good conductor of electricity

In this lab, you will examine the melting points, solubilities, and conductivities of several solids in order to determine the types of bonds they contain. These bonds and the properties they create could make the difference in the way your next grilled cheese sandwich turns out or how warm your house stays on a cold day. Just don't try any bank robberies!

PROCEDURE

Melting Point Observations

❶ Obtain small samples of the three unknown substances provided by your teacher. Put each sample on a separate piece of weighing paper.

❷ Set up an apparatus according to the illustration in Figure 2.

❸ Place a small amount (about the size of an uncooked grain of rice) of unknown 1 in an evaporating dish. Set the dish on the wire gauze and gently heat the contents.

❹ If the unknown does not readily melt, heat it strongly for a minute or two. Describe how easily the substance melts in Table 1.

❺ Repeat steps ❸ and ❹ for unknowns 2 and 3, recording your observations in Table 1.

Figure 2 Setup for testing the melting points of the unknowns

1. The greater the difference in the charge of atoms, the stronger their bonds are. Using the table on the facing page, rank the types of bonds in increasing bond strength, looking specifically at melting points.

   _____

2. Ionic compounds and metallic compounds have higher melting points than covalent compounds. Why do you think this is so?

   _____

   _____

   _____

3. How are network covalent substances different from regular covalent substances when it comes to melting point?

   _____

   _____

   _____

4. On the basis of your observations, make a hypothesis about which unknown is metallic, which is ionic, and which is covalent before you proceed with more testing.

   _____

   _____

   _____

name _____

Solubility Observations

❶ Try to dissolve unknown 1 by placing a small amount of the substance (about the size of a grain of rice) in a test tube and adding about an inch of water. Record the relative solubility in Table 1. You'll need this sample in the next test on conductivity, so don't discard it! Use masking tape to label your test tube.

❷ Repeat step ❶ for unknowns 2 and 3. Record your observations in Table 1. Be sure to save each mixture in separate, labeled test tubes for the conductivity test.

5. Is water a polar or a nonpolar liquid?

   _____

   One general rule about dissolving substances is that "like dissolves like." This means that polar liquids tend to dissolve polar substances and that nonpolar liquids tend to dissolve nonpolar substances. When ionic compounds dissolve in water, they separate out into ions, which are attracted to charged areas on polar molecules.

Keeping Things Straight

To help keep your test tubes, unknowns, and solvents straight, consider using the number code below to label your test tubes, or create your own.

1—unknown 1 in water
2—unknown 2 in water
3—unknown 3 in water
4—unknown 1 in acetone
5—unknown 2 in acetone
6—unknown 3 in acetone

6. Would water be more likely to dissolve ionic or covalent compounds? Explain.

_____

_____

_____

> ⚠️ Before you go on to step ❸, make sure that no one in the lab has a laboratory burner lit. You will be using acetone, a nonpolar liquid used in fingernail polish remover, and it is extremely flammable! You will not need a laboratory burner for the rest of this lab.

❸ Now repeat step ❶ for each unknown, using similar amounts of acetone and unknown as you did for water and unknown. Record your observations in Table 1, and label and save these mixtures.

7. Acetone is a nonpolar liquid. Is it more likely to dissolve ionic or covalent compounds? Explain.

_____

_____

_____

Gotcha Covered
When scientists clean glassware in lab, they often wash it with water and then rinse it with acetone afterward. Why do you think they do this?

8. On the basis of your observations, make a hypothesis about which unknown is metallic, which is ionic, and which is covalent before you proceed with more testing.

_____

_____

_____

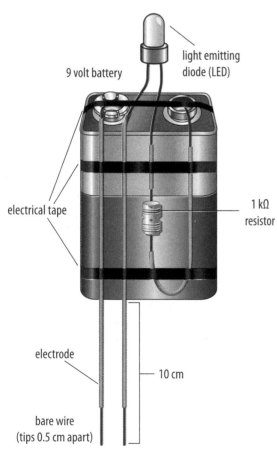

9 volt battery

light emitting diode (LED)

electrical tape

1 kΩ resistor

electrode

10 cm

bare wire (tips 0.5 cm apart)

Figure 3 Conductivity tester and wiring diagram that you will use to test the ability of the unknowns to conduct electricity

Conductivity Observations
Now you will test to see whether your unknowns allow electricity to pass through them, that is, whether they are *conductive*. Electricity is the flow of charge, usually electrons.

❶ Lower the two electrodes of the conductivity tester (Figure 3) into the mixture that you prepared for unknown 1 in step ❶ of your solubility observations. If the sample is conductive, the circuit, or the path of the electricity, will be complete and the light will glow as electricity flows through the circuit. Did the sample conduct electricity? Record your observations in Table 1 (aqueous mixtures).

❷ Repeat step ❶ for the aqueous ("water") mixtures of unknowns 2 and 3. (Remember to rinse the electrodes between tests.) Record your observations in Table 1. Pour your mixtures into the aqueous waste container when you are finished with them.

❸ Repeat step ❶ for the three unknowns, using the acetone mixtures from step ❷ of your solubility observations. Note whether the solutions conduct. Record your observations in Table 1. Pour your mixtures into the acetone waste container when you are finished with them.

❹ Test the conductivity of the remaining small amounts of each unknown solid by touching the electrodes to each one. Record your observations in Table 1.

9. Identify the bond type in each of the three unknowns. Check with your teacher to see if your hypotheses are correct.

_____

_____

10. Did the substances that you used in this lab follow the general rule that "like dissolves like"? Explain.

_____

_____

11. Did the "solution" that you formed by mixing the metal and water conduct electricity? How do your results compare with those for the solid metal?

_____

_____

12. Why does an ionic solid conduct electricity only in the molten state or in an aqueous (water) solution? (*Hint*: Think about electricity as the movement of electrons.)

_____

_____

13. Imagine that ionic compounds such as table salt *did not* dissolve in water. How would that affect your life?

_____

_____

_____

_____

_____

Chemists have created substances with customized physical properties for special uses, such as in airplane wings, electric wires, and insulation for homes. They demonstrate that we can use chemical changes to form bonds that have the properties we need for specific purposes.

14. Describe some examples that show how God uses chemists to provide for our needs.

_____

_____

_____

_____

_____

_____

Table 1			
	Unknown 1	Unknown 2	Unknown 3
Melting			
Solubility in H_2O			
Solubility in CH_3COCH_3 (acetone)			
Conductivity of the aqueous mixtures			
Conductivity of the acetone mixtures			
Conductivity of the solids			

7 ATOMIC ARCHITECTURE
Making Molecular Models

name _____

section _____   date _____

People have been making architectural models for millennia. Architectural models that are hundreds or even thousands of years old have been used to construct buildings such as the Florence cathedral, Cypriot shrines, and Chinese pagodas. Leonardo da Vinci made models of his ideas. These models have been used to construct everything from the Sydney Opera House to airports, towers, and skyscrapers. Modern 3D computer programs enable us to create virtual models that allow virtual tours, such as a tour of the White House or the Louvre in Paris. Models are ways for us to try out new ideas and understand how something that we can't see could work.

Figure 1 On the left is an architectural model of St. Paul's Cathedral. A photo of the actual St. Paul's Cathedral in London is on the right. How do the two compare?

> **Objectives**
> - ✓ Draw Lewis structures of certain molecules.
> - ✓ Relate polar bonds to electro-negativity.
> - ✓ Assemble three-dimensional models of selected molecules.
> - ✓ Visualize molecular polarity from the three-dimensional models.
> - ✓ Relate molecular shape to molecular polarity.

> **Equipment**
> clay
> toothpicks
> molecular modeling kit (optional)
>
>

You are going to make a model of something that you can't see—molecules. Molecules are atoms joined by covalent bonds that form when atoms share electrons in overlapping orbitals. One overlapping set of orbitals forms a single bond, two sets form a double bond, and three sets form a triple bond.

The orbitals in a molecule, both bonded and unbonded, hold electrons. Since like charges repel, orbitals arrange themselves as far apart as possible. This arrangement results in the molecular shapes indicated in Table 1. You can determine the shape of a molecule from its Lewis structure.

Covalent bonds have a spectrum of polarity that is based on the differences of electronegativity between the two atoms. At one end of the spectrum are diatomic elements, which contain completely nonpolar covalent bonds because they form molecules that are made of two of the same atom joined by a

Table 1 Molecular Shapes		
Number of electron regions	Number of bonded nuclei	Geometry
4	4	tetrahedral
	3	pyramidal
	2	bent (109.5°)
	1	linear
3	3	trigonal planar
	2	bent (120°)
	1	linear
2	2	linear
	1	linear

covalent bond (such as N_2). At the other end of the spectrum are molecules like HF, which have two elements with a great difference between their electronegativities.

Polar covalent bonds form when two different atoms in a molecule share electrons, such as the oxygen and hydrogens in water. Because different atoms have different electronegativities, they will not share the electrons equally; therefore, the electrons will be shifted toward the more electronegative atom.

Molecules will also be polar if they contain asymmetrically arranged polar bonds. This shifting of electrons results in a semi-ionic condition that gives the molecule a partially negative pole and a partially positive pole—it is polar. So molecules with mildly covalent bonds act more like diatomic elements, and molecules with highly polarized covalent bonds can act more like ionic compounds.

It is important that you think of molecules as three-dimensional shapes so that you can understand the relationship between regions of electrons, bonded nuclei, molecular shape, and polarity. Although Lewis structures show the arrangements of atoms in a molecule, a physical model of an atom enhances the information in the Lewis structure to give you a sense of the molecule in space. Let's look at an example of how you will do this.

Consider formaldehyde (CH_2O). To make a model of this organic compound, begin by drawing the Lewis structure.

$$\begin{array}{c} H \\ | \\ H-C=\ddot{O}\colon \end{array}$$

After drawing the Lewis dot structure, observe that carbon is the central atom. It has three regions of electrons around it—two bonds to hydrogens and one double bond to oxygen. This double bond is one region of electrons. Now you can make a model showing three regions of electrons that are spaced as far apart as possible. You can see that this

H 2.2																	He
Li 1.0	Be 1.6											B 2.0	C 2.6	N 3.0	O 3.4	F 4.0	Ne
Na 0.9	Mg 1.3											Al 1.6	Si 1.9	P 2.2	S 2.6	Cl 3.2	Ar
K 0.8	Ca 1.0	Sc 1.4	Ti 1.5	V 1.6	Cr 1.7	Mn 1.6	Fe 1.8	Co 1.9	Ni 1.9	Cu 1.9	Zn 1.7	Ga 1.8	Ge 2.0	As 2.2	Se 2.6	Br 3.0	Kr 3.0
Rb 0.8	Sr 1.0	Y 1.2	Zr 1.3	Nb 1.6	Mo 2.2	Tc 1.9	Ru 2.2	Rh 2.3	Pd 2.2	Ag 1.9	Cd 1.7	In 1.8	Sn 2.0	Sb 2.1	Te 2.1	I 2.7	Xe 2.6
Cs 0.8	Ba 0.9	La 1.1	Hf 1.3	Ta 1.5	W 2.4	Re 1.9	Os 2.2	Ir 2.2	Pt 2.3	Au 2.5	Hg 2.0	Tl 1.6	Pb 2.3	Bi 2.0	Po 2.0	At 2.2	Rn
Fr 0.7	Ra 0.9	Ac 1.1	Rf	Db	Sg	Bh	Hs	Mt	Ds	Rg	Cn	Uut	Fl	Uup	Lv	Uus	Uuo

Figure 2 Electronegativities of the elements (shading light to dark indicates increasing electronegativity values). The difference in electronegativity between two atoms determines how polar the covalent bond that connects them will be.

molecule is trigonal planar, and that the molecule contains polar bonds and is a polar molecule.

name _____

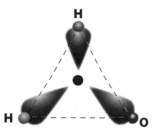

Now, it's your turn to explore some atomic architecture!

PROCEDURE

❶ Gather the materials that you will use to build your models, whether they are clay and toothpicks or molecular models. If you use clay, you will be following an ancient tradition of architectural model-making!

❷ Table 2 on pages 60–61 lists the molecules that you will be assembling. Record your observations and sketch your models in this table.

❸ For each molecule, begin by drawing the Lewis dot structure in Table 2.

❹ Count the regions of electrons around the central atom. A single bond counts as one region, a double bond counts as one region, and each lone pair counts as one region. Record this data in Table 2.

> For a review of how to draw Lewis structures, see pages 155–56 of your textbook.

1. What do you notice about the number of valence electrons of elements that are usually central atoms?

_____

_____

_____

> For a Lewis structure and physical model of germanium fluoride, see Table 7-1 on page 179 of your textbook. It may be handy to have it available while you do this lab.

❺ Identify how many atoms are bonded to the central atom and record the information in Table 2.

❻ Now let's make a model. Use a lump of clay for the central atom, or pick a piece from your kit that has the number of spokes that your central atom can share as bonds. For example, carbon has four spokes since it has four valence electrons and needs four more electrons through sharing in covalent bonds. If you are using clay, pick the number of toothpicks for the number of bonds that your central atom makes. Be sure to leave space in your model for lone pairs if your Lewis structure shows a lone pair on the central atom. Draw a picture of your model and identify its shape in Table 2.

❼ Identify polar bonds in your molecule. Remember that if two different atoms are bonded together, then the bond is polar. Record your observations in Table 2.

> ### *What Are the Types of Molecular Shapes, Again?*
> See Table 7-1 in your textbook for a summary and pictures of bond types to help you answer Questions 2 through 9.

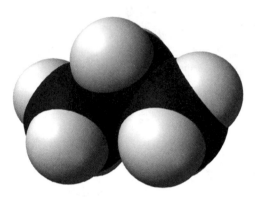

Figure 3 Propane is a hydrocarbon that is often used as a fuel.

2. Why do carbon and hydrogen form a very mildly polar bond (see Figure 2)?

_____

_____

_____

❽ Study the shape of your molecule and the locations of polar bonds to determine whether the entire molecule is polar. Record your ideas in Table 2.

3. Would a molecule containing only carbon and hydrogen, called a *hydrocarbon*, behave more like an ionic compound or more like a diatomic element?

_____

4. If you added a hydrogen ion (H^+) to the ammonia model that you made, what substance would you have? Does this additional hydrogen ion cause the shape of the new molecule to be different from ammonia? Explain.

_____

_____

_____

5. What is the difference between the carbon-oxygen bond in your model of methanol and the one in carbon dioxide?

_____

_____

_____

6. Would a dichloromethane molecule be polar if the hydrogen and chlorine atoms were placed at the corners of a rectangle surrounding the carbon instead of in their actual locations? Explain.

_____

_____

_____

7. Compare the molecular polarity of CCl_4 with CH_2Cl_2. Explain any differences.

_____

_____

_____

8. On the basis of what you have observed, state which molecular shapes will *always* produce polar molecules, assuming that the central atom is bonded to an atom of a different identity.

_____

_____

_____

9. Which molecular shapes will produce nonpolar molecules if the central atom is bonded to atoms of the same element?

_____

_____

_____

Table 2				
IUPAC name	methanal	methane	dihydrogen monoxide	nitrogen trihydride
formula	CH_2O	CH_4	H_2O	NH_3
common name	formaldehyde		water	ammonia
Draw the Lewis dot structure.				
How many regions of electrons surround the central atom?				
How many atoms are bonded to the central atom?				
Make a model of this shape and sketch it.				
What is the molecular shape?				
Does the molecule contain polar bonds?				
Is the entire molecule polar?				

name _____

	Table 2 (continued)				
IUPAC name	carbon dioxide	methanol	hydrogen cyanide	dichloro-methane	carbon tetrachloride
formula	CO_2	CH_3OH	HCN	CH_2Cl_2	CCl_4
common name			cyanide	methylene chloride	
Draw the Lewis dot structure.					
How many regions of electrons surround the central atom?					
How many atoms are bonded to the central atom?					
Make a model of this shape and sketch it.					
What is the molecular shape?					
Does the molecule contain polar bonds?					
Is the entire molecule polar?					

8 CHEMICAL COMPOSITION AND
    REACTIONS

name _____

section _____   date _____

8 EXPEDITIONS IN CHEMICAL EQUATIONS
Chemical Reactions and Equations

Drip, drip, drip. Stalactites grow from the ceiling of a cave, often at a snail's pace of a fraction of a millimeter a year. They form drapery, soda straws, shields, and columns, turning a hole in the ground into a cathedral.

But how do stalactites form? It's all chemistry. When water flows over limestone formations in caves, it dissolves calcium bicarbonate. When this mineral-rich water drips and contacts air, the calcium bicarbonate decomposes into calcium carbonate, water, and carbon dioxide.

$$Ca(HCO_3)_2 \ (aq) \longrightarrow CaCO_3 \ (s) + H_2O \ (l) + CO_2 \ (aq)$$

This is an example of a chemical equation, which you've been learning about in this chapter. The formation of stalactites is a *decomposition reaction*, a reaction in which a single reactant breaks up to produce at least two other substances. By contrast, *synthesis reactions* combine two or more substances into a single product. *Replacement reactions* involve compounds that swap ions and often produce a precipitate. In a *single* replacement reaction, an active element takes the place of a less active element in a compound. In a *double* replacement reaction, two compounds swap elements with each other.

In this experiment, you will create a series of different types of reactions involving copper and some of its compounds. For each chemical reaction involved, you will write a chemical equation. See what kinds of interesting things can happen when you take an expedition in chemical equations!

Figure 1 Stalactites in caves are the result of a decomposition chemical reaction.

Objectives
✓ Perform chemical reactions.
✓ Record the changes that take place during chemical reactions.
✓ Write chemical equations to describe chemical reactions.

Equipment
beaker, 150 mL
beaker, 250 mL
graduated cylinder, 10 mL
graduated cylinder, 25 mL
laboratory burner and lighter
ring stand and ring
wire gauze
clay triangle
crucible
crucible tongs
filtering funnel
filter paper
glass stirring rod
copper wool
sodium hydroxide (NaOH), 3 *M*
sulfuric acid (H_2SO_4), 2 *M*
waste container

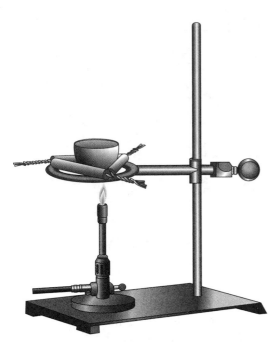

Figure 2 Crucible setup

PROCEDURE

Synthesis Reaction

❶ Make a loose wad of copper wool and place it in the crucible.

❷ Set up an apparatus as shown in Figure 2. Place the crucible, uncovered, on a clay triangle and heat it strongly for about 5 minutes until the copper is no longer present. A black product results from the reaction of copper with atmospheric oxygen.

1. What is the black product that resulted from the reaction of copper and atmospheric oxygen?

   _____

2. Describe anything else that you observed during the reaction.

   _____

   _____

   _____

3. Write a word equation and a balanced equation for the synthesis reaction in which copper and atmospheric oxygen produced the black compound.

   _____

   _____

Copper would react with oxygen if it was just left out in the air, right? Think about how temperature speeds up the motion of particles.

4. Why do you think heating up the copper sped up the reaction between copper and oxygen to produce the black compound?

   _____

   _____

   _____

Double Replacement Reaction 1

❶ Using crucible tongs, dump the black product from the crucible into the 150 mL beaker.

❷ Pour 5 mL of 2 M H_2SO_4 into the 10 mL graduated cylinder.

❸ Add the sulfuric acid to the black product in the beaker, and carefully stir the mixture with the glass stirring rod. Some of the black product will dissolve in the sulfuric acid. You may need to give this solution a minute or two to react.

5. What two products resulted from the addition of sulfuric acid to the black compound?

   _____

6. Describe anything else that you observed during the reaction.

_____

_____

_____

❹ Place the filtering funnel in the clay triangle and set it on the ring. Fold a piece of filter paper and place it in the funnel.

❺ Filter the solution into the 250 mL beaker and save the filtrate in the beaker for step ❶ below. The filter paper can be thrown out. Put a piece of paper under the beaker containing the filtrate.

7. What was the color of the solution after the sulfuric acid was added to the black compound and it was filtered?

_____

8. Write a word equation and a balanced equation for the double replacement reaction resulting from the addition of sulfuric acid to the black compound.

_____

_____

_____

9. What ion do you think caused the color change of the solution of sulfuric acid and the black compound? What evidence do you have for your answer?

_____

_____

_____

_____

_____

Double Replacement Reaction 2

❶ Pour approximately 20 mL of 3 M NaOH into the 25 mL graduated cylinder.

❷ Add 10 mL of the sodium hydroxide from the graduated cylinder to the filtrate in the beaker gradually as you stir the mixture with the glass stirring rod. A precipitate will form.

❸ Add additional sodium hydroxide while you continue to stir the mixture until no more precipitate forms.

10. What were the two products that resulted from the double replacement reaction of sodium hydroxide and the filtrate?

_____

11. Describe anything else that you observed during the reaction.

_____

_____

_____

12. Write a word equation and a balanced equation for the double replacement reaction resulting from the addition of sodium hydroxide to the colored filtrate.

_____

_____

_____

Decomposition Reaction

❶ Replace the clay triangle on the ring with the wire gauze. Place the beaker containing the mixture from the previous procedure on the gauze and *cautiously* heat the mixture until it boils. (Alkaline solutions tend to spatter!) Stir constantly until a reaction takes place. Water and copper (II) oxide will form.

13. When you heated the mixture, what compound decomposed into copper (II) oxide (CuO) and water?

_____

14. Describe anything else that you observed during the reaction.

_____

_____

_____

_____

15. Write a word equation and a balanced equation for the decomposition reaction resulting in the products copper (II) oxide and water.

_____

_____

_____

❷ Pour the mixture from step ❶ into the waste container provided.

⚠ Watch Out for Spatters!

Make sure that you are wearing gloves, goggles, and an apron when you heat this caustic solution. If it spatters and lands on your skin, it could cause a chemical burn. If this happens, go to your teacher, who can rinse the area with a boric acid solution that will neutralize the base so that it will stop stinging and burning your skin.

Figure 3 Copper (II) oxide, also called cupric oxide, is often used to produce rayon, solar panels, and glazes in pottery.

16. What substance was present in your mixture from the second double replacement reaction that did not participate in the decomposition reaction?

name _____

_____

_____

_____

17. If you had filtered out the precipitate produced in the second double replacement reaction, would you have gotten the same results in your decomposition reaction? Why or why not?

_____

_____

_____

_____

_____

18. Compare the result of your last decomposition reaction with the result of your first synthesis reaction. Did you observe any similarities in these two substances?

_____

_____

Stalactites don't just form in caves; they can form under old buildings, especially those made of marble. Under the Lincoln Memorial there are stalactites over 5 feet long!

19. Look at the chemical equation for this process on page 63. Suggest a way to prevent this from happening.

_____

_____

_____

_____

_____

20. How can chemical reactions like the four you have done be useful to people?

_____

_____

_____

_____

9 CHEMICAL CALCULATIONS

9A TORCHING METALS
Empirical Formulas

name _____

section _____ date _____

Joseph Proust was on to something. In his apothecary lab, he had been experimenting with different metals, such as metal oxides and carbonates. He found that naturally occurring copper carbonate had the same proportions of elements as the copper carbonate that he made in the lab. In other words, he concluded, the proportions needed to form a particular compound had to be constant and definite! His findings led to the *law of definite composition*, also known as *Proust's law*.

Figure 1 Joseph Proust, chemist and apothecary

The law of definite composition states that the ratio of elements in a compound is constant for every particle of that compound. These ratios can be expressed by formulas. For example, the compound potassium chlorate is made up of potassium chlorate molecules. Each molecule has a ratio of 1 potassium atom to 1 chlorine atom to 3 oxygen atoms, or 1:1:3. We express this in the formula $KClO_3$. Since this formula expresses the simplest whole-number ratio for potassium chlorate, it is potassium chlorate's *empirical formula*. Sometimes the empirical formula is the same thing as the molecular formula, as with potassium chlorate and water. But other times the molecular formula and the empirical formula are different, such as with glucose ($C_6H_{12}O_6$ and CH_2O).

In this lab, you will be making metal oxides just like Proust did. You will determine empirical formulas experimentally by establishing the mass of each element present in the compound. To do this, you will synthesize magnesium oxide from its elements, magnesium and oxygen. You will also determine the mass of the *magnesium* before the synthesis and the mass of the *magnesium oxide* after the synthesis. Subtracting the mass of the magnesium from the mass of the magnesium oxide gives you the mass of the oxygen used in the synthesis reaction. From these masses you can find the number of moles of each element. Since the mole ratio must equal the ratio of atoms in the compound, you can easily find the empirical formula.

PROCEDURE

Setting Up

❶ Clean your crucible and crucible cover with a damp paper towel. Support them on a ring with a clay triangle. The crucible cover should be tilted on the top of the crucible, leaving a small opening (see Figure 2 on the next page).

❷ Heat the crucible and crucible cover for several minutes to drive off any moisture. Allow the crucible to cool until it is comfortable to the touch.

❸ When it is cool, find the mass of the crucible with its cover to the nearest 0.01 g and record it in Table 1.

Objectives
✓ Write chemical equations after observing chemical reactions.
✓ Relate the law of definite composition to atomic masses.
✓ Calculate percent composition.
✓ Experimentally determine an empirical formula.

Equipment
laboratory scale (accurate to 0.01 g)
laboratory burner and lighter
clay triangle
crucible and cover
crucible tongs
ring stand and ring
magnesium ribbon (30 cm)
sandpaper
transfer pipet (eyedropper)

⚠ Burn Warning!
Be very careful when handling hot glassware and crucibles in this lab! Don't just grab anything if it is something that you have heated up previously. Put your hand near an object to feel whether it's hot before attempting to touch it. If you do get a burn, relieve the burn immediately by immersing in water, and tell your teacher.

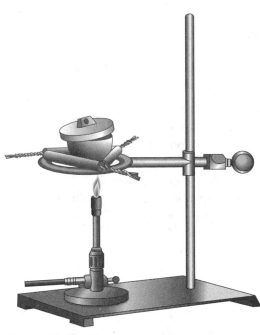

Figure 2 Crucible and cover apparatus

⚠ From this point forward, handle the crucible and its cover with the crucible tongs!

Figure 3 Because of its flammability, magnesium is often used in fire starters.

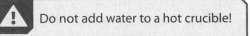

⚠ Do not add water to a hot crucible!

❹ Clean a strip of magnesium ribbon approximately 30 cm long with sandpaper to remove the oxide coating; then wipe it off with a dry paper towel.

1. Why is it necessary to remove any existing oxide coating from the magnesium ribbon before performing the experiment?

_____

_____

_____

_____

❺ Roll up the magnesium ribbon into a tight spiral and place it flat on the bottom of the crucible. It's important that the magnesium be heated uniformly so that it reacts completely.

❻ Replace the cover on the crucible and find the mass of the crucible, cover, and magnesium to the nearest 0.01 g. Record the result in Table 1.

❼ Calculate the mass of magnesium by subtracting the mass that you determined in step ❸ from the mass you determined in step ❻. Record the result in Table 1.

Making Magnesium Oxide

❶ Place the crucible and its contents on the clay triangle and begin heating them. You should remove the cover but hold it nearby with tongs. Use the cover only to stop flare-ups and to keep the magnesium burning in a controlled way. ***The moment the magnesium starts to burn, place the cover on the crucible.***

❷ Continue taking the cover on and off every 1–2 minutes using crucible tongs until the magnesium fails to glow when the cover is removed. At this point, heat the covered crucible as hot as possible for several additional minutes.

2. Why do you need to keep taking the cover on and off?

_____

_____

_____

_____

❸ Allow the covered crucible to cool for about 10 minutes. It will cool faster if allowed to do so on a wire gauze square placed on the desktop. Answer the questions that follow while the crucible cools.

3. Write the balanced equation for the reaction of magnesium with oxygen gas to form magnesium oxide. Since atmospheric oxygen is a diatomic element, use O_2 in the reaction. What do you predict will be the empirical formula of magnesium oxide?

name _____

_____

_____

_____

Air is a mixture of mostly nitrogen and oxygen gases. When magnesium burns in air, most of the magnesium combines with oxygen to form magnesium oxide; however, some of the magnesium combines with nitrogen to form magnesium nitride (Mg_3N_2). So what you have in your crucible right now is a mixture of magnesium oxide and magnesium nitride. We need it all to be magnesium oxide.

4. Suggest a general way to deal with the magnesium nitride.

_____

_____

To deal with the magnesium nitride, you will add water. This step will convert the magnesium nitride to magnesium hydroxide and ammonia gas (NH_3).

5. Write the balanced equation for the reaction between magnesium nitride and water.

_____

We still have a problem though! Instead of a mixture of magnesium oxide and magnesium *nitride*, now we have a mixture of magnesium oxide and magnesium *hydroxide*. But there's a very easy way to fix this. If we heat magnesium hydroxide, it decomposes into solid magnesium oxide and water vapor.

6. Write the balanced equation for the decomposition of magnesium hydroxide.

_____

❹ Now, let's do what you just wrote about. ***Make sure that your crucible is cool enough to touch.*** Using the transfer pipet, add 10 drops of water uniformly over the crucible's contents.

❺ Carefully heat the crucible without its cover until the water evaporates; then heat strongly for several minutes.

7. Do you detect any recognizable odor? If so, describe the odor and see if you can identify what the substance is.

_____

_____

_____

❻ Cool the crucible for about 5 minutes. Repeat steps ❸ and ❹ again. The contents of the crucible should now be pure magnesium oxide.

> ### Magnesium Fires
> Since magnesium is extremely flammable, magnesium fires cannot be put out with water or even carbon dioxide fire extinguishers; both of these substances make magnesium fires worse. They are usually put out with dry sand or other special fire extinguishers designed to extinguish metal fires.

❼ Allow the crucible, the cover, and the contents to cool to room temperature, and then find their combined mass to the nearest 0.01 g. Record the result in Table 1.

❽ To make sure that the water is entirely gone, reheat the covered crucible for several minutes, cool it to room temperature, and find the combined mass again. Record it in Table 1. It should be very close (within a few hundredths of a gram) to the one obtained in step ❼. If it is not, repeat this step until you obtain two masses that agree.

❾ Use the lower of the two masses of the crucible, cover, and contents from Table 1 to calculate the mass of the magnesium oxide. Record the result in Table 1.

❿ Finally, calculate the mass of the oxygen that chemically combined with the magnesium to form magnesium oxide. Record this value in Table 1.

8. Use your starting mass of magnesium and your mass of oxygen to calculate the moles of O and Mg. You can show your work in the margin.

_____

_____

_____

9. Divide both mole values by the smaller value to get the ratio in whole numbers. If needed, show your work in the margin.

_____

10. Determine the empirical formula for magnesium oxide. Was it what you predicted in Question 3?

_____

_____

_____

11. Using the masses of magnesium and magnesium oxide obtained during the experiment, calculate the observed (experimental) percent composition of magnesium in your magnesium oxide.

_____

12. Calculate the actual percent composition of magnesium in magnesium oxide from the formula MgO by assuming a 1 mol sample. (See Example Problem 9-6 on page 231 of your textbook.)

_____

Remember to consider significant digits when calculating your percent composition of magnesium.

13. Calculate your percent error using the formula for percent error given below.

$$\text{Percent error} = \frac{|\text{actual value} - \text{measured value}|}{\text{actual value}} \times 100\%$$

_____

14. How does this experiment demonstrate the law of definite composition?

_____

_____

_____

Table 1	
Mass of crucible and cover	
Mass of crucible, cover, and magnesium	
Mass of magnesium	
Mass of crucible, cover, and magnesium oxide—first mass	
Mass of crucible, cover, and magnesium oxide—second mass	
Mass of magnesium oxide produced	
Mass of oxygen	

9B Water . . . Water!
Formulas of Hydrates

name _____

section _____ date _____

Sputter . . . cough . . . stall. Your Jeep has just run out of gasoline in the middle of the Sahara Desert. You reach for your canteen, suddenly feeling thirsty. It's empty. "NO!" your voice echoes into the arid hills. You are in danger of death by dehydration!

Did you know that chemical compounds can get dehydrated too? A *hydrate* is a compound, usually a salt, that has water molecules trapped in its crystalline structure. When the salt and water unite, they do so in a specific ratio because there are certain empty places in the crystal lattice that can be filled with water molecules. For example, calcium sulfate dihydrate, also known as gypsum, contains 1 mole of the salt $CaSO_4$ for every 2 moles of water. This produces the hydrate $CaSO_4 \cdot 2H_2O$.

The water that is incorporated into the crystal structure of a hydrate is called the *water of hydration*. Waters of hydration can be driven out of a hydrate by low pressures or high temperatures, though some hydrates lose some or all of their waters of hydration naturally. These hydrates are said to be *efflorescent*. Gypsum ($CaSO_4 \cdot 2H_2O$) can experience efflorescence. There are also substances that attract water when placed in the open air at room temperature. These substances are called *hygroscopic* compounds. They don't experience any noticeable change at first when they absorb water from their surroundings, though they can eventually cake up. Salt is hygroscopic, which is why salt shakers in restaurants also contain uncooked rice as an anticaking agent.

In this experiment, you will use heat to drive off the waters of hydration in a hydrated salt, effectively dehydrating it. When a hydrated salt is heated, the products are water (which is driven off) and an *anhydrous* salt, or the salt without any of its waters of hydration. By determining the moles of anhydrous salt left and the moles of water driven off, you can determine the formula of the hydrate.

Objectives
✓ Relate the chemical and physical properties of hydrated compounds to their chemical structure.
✓ Determine the formula of a hydrated compound by heating it and measuring how much water is released and how much anhydrous salt is left.

Equipment
laboratory scale (accurate to 0.01 g)
laboratory burner and lighter
clay triangle
crucible
crucible tongs
ring stand and ring
hydrated salt
beaker, 10 mL

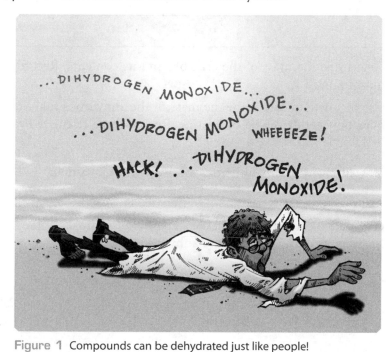

Figure 1 Compounds can be dehydrated just like people!

Figure 2 Sometimes hydrated salts are a different color than their anhydrous form. Cobalt (II) chloride hexahydrate (top) is red, while anhydrous cobalt (II) chloride (bottom) is blue.

Remember significant digits!

PROCEDURE

Setting Up

❶ Obtain 2.00–3.00 g of a hydrate. Ask your teacher for its anhydrous formula. Record the formula in Table 1.

❷ Clean your crucible with a damp paper towel. Support it on a ring with the clay triangle.

❸ Heat the crucible for several minutes to drive off any moisture. Allow the crucible to cool until it is comfortable to the touch.

❹ When it is cool, find the mass of the crucible to the nearest 0.01 g and record it in Table 1.

❺ Add your hydrate sample to the crucible. Determine the mass of the sample in the crucible and record it in Table 1.

❻ Calculate the amount of hydrated salt that you are starting with and record it in Table 1.

Getting Dehydrated

❶ Place the crucible on the clay triangle. Heat it over a low flame, then gradually raise the temperature. Continue to heat it for 15 minutes.

❷ Allow the crucible to cool to room temperature or until it is comfortable to the touch.

1. Did your salt hydrate change color when you heated it? If so, why do you think this happened?

_____

_____

_____

_____

_____

❸ Determine the mass of the crucible and its contents. Record this mass in Table 1.

❹ Use this data to determine the mass of the anhydrous salt and the mass of water driven off by heating. Record these calculated values in Table 1.

2. How many moles of anhydrous salt were in your sample?

_____

❺ Calculate the number of moles of water in the original sample using the weights of the hydrous and anhydrous salts.

3. How many moles of water were in your sample?

   _____

4. What is the ratio of moles of water that would combine with 1 mole of the anhydrous salt? (Express to the proper number of decimal places.)

   _____

5. Round the value obtained in Question 4 to the nearest whole number.

   _____

6. Give the formula of your hydrate.

   _____

7. What is the name of your hydrate?

   _____

8. Using your experimental value and the exact value for the number of waters of hydration supplied by your teacher, calculate your percent error.

$$\text{Percent error} = \frac{\left|\text{actual value} - \text{measured value}\right|}{\text{actual value}} \times 100\%$$

   _____

   _____

9. Would insufficient heating of the hydrate make your experimental value of the waters of hydration in Question 5 too large or too small? Explain your reasoning.

   _____

   _____

   _____

In the rock under the bottom of the ocean floor in various places in the world, there are gas hydrates of methane, called *methane clathrates*, which trap methane gas in a water crystal lattice. This is ice that can burn!

10. What would it take to free this methane? Is it likely that this would happen? Why or why not?

_____

_____

_____

_____

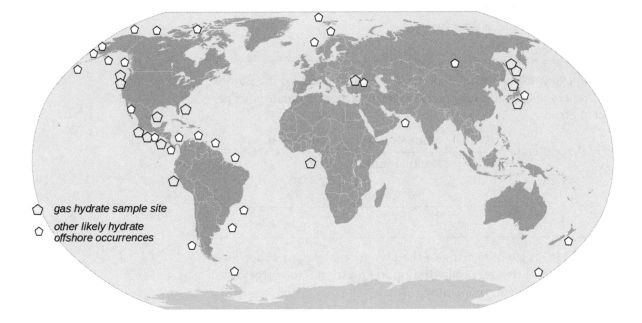

gas hydrate sample site

other likely hydrate offshore occurrences

Figure 3 Location of methane clathrates around the world

Table 1	
Formula of anhydrous salt	
Mass of crucible	
Mass of crucible and hydrated salt	
Mass of hydrated salt	
Mass of crucible and anhydrous salt	
Mass of anhydrous salt	
Mass of water released	

9C CHYMESTRY
Stoichiometric Relationships

name _____

section _____   date _____

Your stomach is a scary place. When food particles enter it, they encounter an alien environment of gastric acids and enzymes that turn them into pulp. Gastric acids are fairly strong, with a pH of 1–2, and they are mostly hydrochloric acid (HCl). You'll learn more about this acid and others in Chapter 16. The semi-liquid, half-digested food pulp that gastric acids help produce is called *chyme* (pronounced *kime*).

So what happens when this acidic chyme leaves your stomach and enters the small intestine? If nothing happened, you could have some highly unpleasant feelings! At the beginning of your small intestine, however, your pancreas injects some sodium bicarbonate, or sodium hydrogen carbonate ($NaHCO_3$)—you know this as baking soda. You've already experimented a bit with baking soda in Lab 1A, "The Great Biscuit Bake-Off." Baking soda reacts with the HCl in your gastric acids so that they don't irritate the rest of your digestive system.

In this lab you are going to re-create the contents of your small intestine! You will be reacting HCl with sodium bicarbonate to see what happens. The goal is for you to measure the mole ratios of the reactants and the products so that you can figure out what the stoichiometric relationships are in the balanced chemical reaction of these two substances. Your pancreas needs to know how much sodium bicarbonate to produce to neutralize your stomach acid, so this is important! You will measure the masses of both products and reactants to help you measure the mole ratios of the reactants and products.

Objective
✓ Relate the moles of reactant and the moles of product in a chemical reaction.

Equipment
laboratory scale (accurate to 0.01 g)
beaker, 150 mL
laboratory burner and lighter
crucible tongs
evaporating dish
ring stand and ring
spatula
test tube
transfer pipet
wash bottle
watch glass, small
weighing paper
wire gauze
hydrochloric acid (HCl), 6 *M*
sodium bicarbonate ($NaHCO_3$)

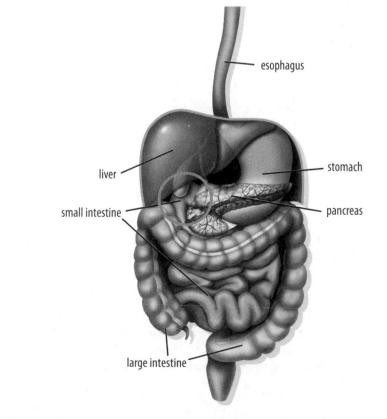

esophagus

liver

small intestine

stomach

pancreas

large intestine

Figure 1 The place where the stomach meets the small intestine is where the reaction of HCl and $NaHCO_3$ occurs.

PROCEDURE

Setting Up

❶ Clean an evaporating dish and rinse it with water from a wash bottle.

❷ Using the crucible tongs, hold the evaporating dish in a well-adjusted burner flame for several minutes to remove all the moisture.

❸ While the dish is cooling on the wire gauze, use a spatula to place some sodium bicarbonate on a piece of weighing paper.

❹ When the dish is cool, measure its mass. Record this value to the nearest 0.01 g in Table 1.

1. Why is it important for the evaporating dish to be cool and dry?

    _____

    _____

    _____

❺ Using the spatula, add about 3 g of the $NaHCO_3$ to the evaporating dish while it is still on the balance. Record the combined mass of the dish and $NaHCO_3$ to the nearest 0.01 g in Table 1.

❻ Calculate the amount of sodium bicarbonate and record it in Table 1.

You are about to combine sodium bicarbonate with hydrochloric acid. Think about this reaction. It's very similar to the reaction that people create in homemade volcanoes with vinegar and baking soda—it makes a lot of fizz.

2. Write down the chemical reaction of $NaHCO_3$ with HCl, predicting what you think the products will be.

    _____

    _____

    _____

    _____

Reacting NaHCO₃ with HCl

❶ Cover the evaporating dish with a small watch glass to keep chemicals from spattering during the reaction.

❷ Pour about 6 mL of 6 *M* HCl into a clean test tube. Gradually add the acid to the $NaHCO_3$ with a transfer pipet or dropper. Allow the drops to enter the lip of the evaporating dish so that they flow down the side *gradually and slowly* (see Figure 2).

❸ Continue adding the acid drop by drop until the reaction stops and there is no more fizzing. Do not add more acid than is necessary. Tilt the dish from side to side to make sure that the acid has reached all the solid.

Figure 2 This is how you *slowly* add acid with a pipet.

3. What substance do you think is producing the fizzing that you are observing?

name _____

_____

There are actually two reactions going on here. In the first reaction the hydrochloric acid reacts with the sodium bicarbonate to produce sodium chloride and carbonic acid. In the second reaction, the carbonic acid decomposes to form carbon dioxide gas and water. So the fizz that you are seeing is carbon dioxide gas escaping. What you have left in your evaporating dish is a mix of salt and water—salt from the sodium chloride and hydrochloric acid reaction, and water from the decomposition of the carbonic acid.

❹ Remove the watch glass and, using a wash bottle of water, rinse any spattered material from the underside of the watch glass with a small amount of distilled water. Be careful to wash all the material into the evaporating dish so that no NaCl is lost (see Figure 3).

4. Write the balanced equation for the reaction between sodium bicarbonate and hydrochloric acid to produce sodium chloride and carbonic acid.

_____

5. Write the balanced equation for the decomposition of carbonic acid.

_____

Figure 3 Carefully rinse the watch glass with water so that no NaCl is lost.

6. Now, add these two equations together, canceling out any products from the first reaction that were consumed in the second reaction.

_____

7. What do you predict will be the stoichiometric ratio of sodium bicarbonate to sodium chloride? How do you know?

_____

_____

Finding the Mass of NaCl

Let's see if you're right! Now you are going to boil off the water to determine the mass of NaCl formed in your reaction.

❶ Place the evaporating dish, supported by the wire gauze, on the ring stand (see Figure 4). Heat the water in the evaporating dish until it boils gently. Do not let the water boil over or you will lose some of the NaCl and spoil the experiment.

❷ Continue to heat the dish until most of the water has evaporated. Use an air bath to dry the NaCl completely.

❸ Remove the dish from the air bath and allow it to cool; then weigh it and record its mass to the nearest 0.01 g in Table 1.

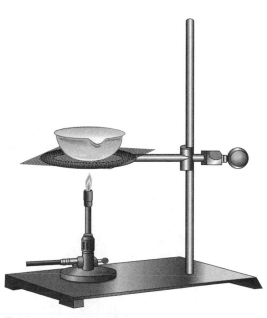

Figure 4 Set up an air bath to boil off the water that remains after your reaction.

❹ To make sure that all the water has been driven off, reheat the dish and contents directly on the wire gauze. Let them cool and weigh them again. Record your result in Table 1. If this mass does not closely agree with the mass in step ❸, reheat, cool, and continue measuring the mass until you achieve a consistent measurement.

❺ Use the lower of the two values for the mass of the evaporating dish and your sodium chloride and record it in Table 1.

❻ Use this information to calculate the mass of NaCl produced and record it in Table 1.

8. Calculate the number of moles of $NaHCO_3$ used and NaCl produced in the reaction. Show your setups in the margin.

_____

9. Divide both mole amounts of $NaHCO_3$ and NaCl by the smaller of the two to give your experimental ratio between $NaHCO_3$ and NaCl (x:1 or 1:x). Report your mole ratio of $NaHCO_3$ to NaCl.

_____

10. How did this ratio compare to what you predicted in Question 7?

_____

_____

11. So what did you use to determine the stoichiometric ratios between $NaHCO_3$ and NaCl?

_____

_____

Table 1	
Mass of evaporating dish	
Mass of evaporating dish plus $NaHCO_3$	
Mass of $NaHCO_3$	
Mass of evaporating dish plus NaCl—weighing 1	
Mass of evaporating dish plus NaCl—weighing 2	
Mass of NaCl	

9D CRACKING THE KERNEL
Inquiring into Percent Composition

name _____

section _____ date _____

There's nothing like a good movie and a bowl of popcorn. It's a bit of a mystery how a hard seed can turn into a puffy morsel of yumminess with just the application of heat. How does this happen?

A popcorn kernel contains moisture (water) within its starchy endosperm. The outer covering of the kernel, or pericarp, is tough and moisture resistant. When sufficiently heated, the water inside turns to steam within the strong outer hull, which normally does not allow its escape. This superheated, pressurized steam softens the starch in the endosperm. But as the temperature continues to increase, eventually the pressure of the steam becomes high enough to suddenly burst the hull, allowing the steam to escape and the starchy interior to expand rapidly and form a foam. Once the pressure is released, the foam cools rapidly, allowing it to set in the shape that we recognize as popped corn.

The rate at which the popcorn kernel is heated is an important consideration in obtaining good yields of popped corn. If it is heated too rapidly, the bursting point of the hull is reached before the starch is softened sufficiently; the result is a partially popped kernel with a hard center. If it is heated too slowly, the steam that forms may leak out of weaker areas of the hull before the pressure builds sufficiently to cause the kernel to burst. The result is unpopped kernels.

PROCEDURE

You get to design your own procedure! Your goal: *Find out how much water is in a kernel of popcorn by calculating the percent composition by mass.* As you do, consider the points below. When you are ready, outline your steps in the space at the end of this lab and ask your teacher to approve your methods.

❶ You may want to use a small number of kernels to make it easier to count.

❷ It may be a good idea to do your experiment several times to confirm your results.

❸ Consider using vegetable oil in the container that you heat to prevent the kernels and the popped corn from burning. To do this, pour in enough oil to cover the bottom of the container.

❹ Be sure to provide an escape for the steam from the container as it is heated. At the same time, you should provide a way to limit the loss of oil by spattering—and to prevent the escape of popped corn!

❺ Burned popcorn smells terrible! Be careful not to burn it.

❻ (Optional) Your teacher may also provide old (presumably drier) kernels to compare with fresher kernels in terms of both percent composition and popping success rate. If directed, you should devise a procedure that will examine these relationships between the fresh and the old kernels.

Objectives

✓ Learn about percent composition as applied to a familiar item—popcorn.

✓ (Optional) Compare the effect of age on popcorn's percent composition and on its ability to pop.

Equipment

popcorn kernels
equipment determined by students

Figure 1 All this came out of a few kernels of corn?

⚠ Safety Information

Be sure to get your procedure approved by your teacher before you begin. Plan to observe safety considerations! There is a potential for burns and injury in this lab if not done properly.

Do not eat the popcorn since you will be using equipment that may be contaminated by chemicals.

THINK ABOUT IT

1. It occurs to someone that the unpopped kernels could be eliminated from a batch of popcorn by using a machine to automatically cut a small slit in each kernel before popping to help get the kernel started in its explosion. Comment on this idea and its potential for success.

_____

_____

_____

_____

_____

_____

2. Some evidence shows that popcorn has been a snack favorite for hundreds of years. What do you think would happen to popcorn kernels that were dated to about 1770 if you tried to pop them? Explain your answer.

_____

_____

_____

_____

_____

_____

3. List several possible sources of procedural error that may affect the reliability of your data.

_____

_____

_____

_____

YOUR PLAN

name _____

_____

_____

_____

_____

_____

_____

_____

_____

YOUR FINDINGS

_____

_____

_____

_____

_____

_____

_____

_____

_____

10 GASES

10A THE TEMPERATURE CLIFF
Finding Absolute Zero

name _____

section _____ date _____

In 1665 Robert Boyle suggested that there was a temperature cliff, or a *primum frigidum*, below which it was impossible to go. Today, we know this rock-bottom temperature as *absolute zero*. For centuries, people theorized about the existence of absolute zero and made guesses about its value on various temperature scales. In 1848 Kelvin devised his temperature scale, placing absolute zero at the lowest end. Since then, scientists have pushed to try to get as close as possible to absolute zero. They theorize that there could be temperatures in space that are smaller than a quadrillionth of a kelvin.

In this lab, you will trap a volume of air in a capillary tube and relate the height of the column to its temperature. The height of this column of air is related to its volume because the diameter of the capillary tube is essentially constant over the entire length of the tube. Thus, in the formula for the volume of a cylinder ($V = \pi r^2 h$), πr^2 is constant; the volume of trapped air will be proportional to the height of the column. You will use this data to do something early scientists did—plot data on graph paper and extrapolate to determine absolute zero.

Objectives

✓ Conduct an experiment that changes a column of air at constant pressure by changing its temperature.

✓ Predict changes in a column of air at a constant pressure.

✓ Use changes of height in an air column to experimentally determine absolute zero.

Equipment

laboratory burner and lighter
laboratory thermometer (accurate to 0.1 °C)
crucible tongs
beaker, 1000 mL
metric ruler
watch glass
glass stirring rod
melting point capillary tubes (2)
masking tape
vegetable oil
ice cubes

Figure 1 In 2003 Deborah Jin formed a new sixth state of matter, the *fermionic condensate*, after she cooled potassium atoms to 0.00000005 K.

PROCEDURE

Setting Up

❶ Pour about 10 drops of vegetable oil onto the watch glass. Light the laboratory burner.

❷ Carefully hold one of the capillary tubes in the tongs with the open end slanted upward, and pass the entire length through the burner flame several times. Immediately dip the open end of this heated

If you allow the tube to get too hot, the length of trapped air column will be too small, resulting in larger relative errors. If you do not heat the capillary tube enough, the air column will be too long, making it impossible for you to obtain data at higher temperatures.

tube into the oil on the watch glass and allow it to cool and draw up a "plug" of oil about 1 cm long. You may need to hold the tube in the oil for a second or two to draw it up. When cooled to room temperature, the length of the column of trapped air should be about 5–7 cm.

❸ Repeat step ❷ with the second capillary tube.

1. What is the purpose of the oil plug?

   _____

   _____

2. Describe the temperature, pressure, and volume conditions inside the capillary tube.

   _____

   _____

   _____

   _____

   _____

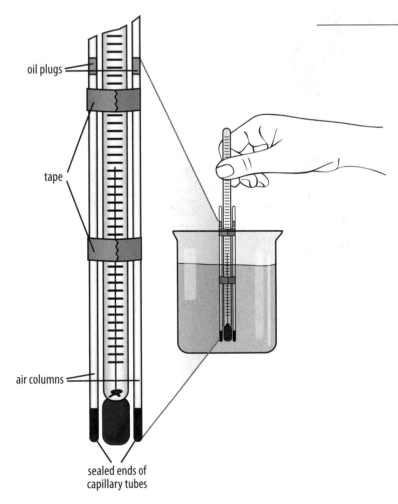

oil plugs

tape

air columns

sealed ends of capillary tubes

❹ Attach the capillary tubes containing trapped air—with their open ends upward—to the thermometer using small pieces of tape, as shown in Figure 2.

3. Why did you leave one end of the capillary tube open?

   _____

   _____

   _____

   _____

4. Which gas law applies to this condition?

   _____

❺ Fill the beaker about two-thirds full of water and ice. Hold the thermometer in the water close to the beaker wall so that you can read the temperature scale and see the location of the oil plugs in the capillary tubes. The entire air column should be submerged, but the open ends of the capillary tubes must stay above the water line.

Figure 2 This is the setup you will use to determine the value of absolute zero.

Getting Numbers

❶ Now, wait. Hold the assembly in the ice-water bath until the temperature reaches a steady reading. Stirring the bath periodically with a stirring rod will speed up this process.

5. Why do you think stirring the ice-water bath speeds up the leveling off of the temperature change?

_____

_____

_____

_____

6. Predict the temperature for the air column after it stops changing in the ice-water bath. This is the starting temperature (t_1).

_____

❷ Once you have noted no further change in the thermometer, record the temperature to the nearest 0.1 °C in Table 1.

❸ Wait an additional minute. Carefully place the ruler in the water next to one of the capillary tubes. Line up the *0* with the top of the melted glass (the start of the air column). Determine the height of the air column to the nearest 0.1 cm. Measure from the top of the melted glass to the bottom of the oil plug. Do *not* include either the melted glass itself or the oil plug in the measurement. Record your result in Table 1. Repeat for the other capillary tube.

> ### Measuring the Air Column
> In this cold-water bath, you will probably need to wipe the condensation from the beaker to get a clear view of the capillary tubes. Put the ruler into the water with the capillary tubes to measure the height of the air column. When you measure the height of the column, be sure not to include the oil plug.

7. Why do you measure from the bottom of the oil meniscus to the top of the thickened glass seal at the end of the tube?

_____

_____

8. What are some possible sources of error in your measurement of the air column?

_____

_____

❹ Empty the beaker and refill it with cold tap water. Hold the assembly in the water as you did in step ❶.

❺ Wait until 1 minute after the thermometer has stopped changing. Again, record the temperature and the height of the two air columns in Table 1.

❻ Empty the beaker and refill it with warm tap water. Repeat step ❺ and record your results in Table 1.

❼ Repeat the procedure one more time with the hottest tap water you can obtain. Record your results in Table 1. You should have four temperature and height measurements. This will give you data at four temperatures in the range of 0–50 °C.

Number Crunching

❶ On the graphing area on the facing page, plot the Celsius temperatures on the *x*-axis and the height values on the *y*-axis. Plot both sets of height and temperature values using different colors for the data points for each tube. Color in the blocks in Table 1 labeled "Tube 1" and "Tube 2" to help you remember which data color goes with each tube.

❷ Using a ruler, draw a straight line that best fits each set of four points obtained for each tube using the colored pencil that corresponds to the color of the points. Extend them to the left (extrapolate) until they cross the *x*-axis. This value of *x* is your value for absolute zero.

9. What do the graphs look like?

_____

_____

❸ Determine the value of absolute zero for each line. Average the two values and round the result to the nearest 1 °C.

10. Report the value you found for absolute zero.

_____

_____

11. Calculate the percent error for your value, using −273 °C as the theoretical, or actual value, of absolute zero.

_____

_____

12. When you extend your graph to try to figure out the temperature for absolute zero, what is the height of the air column that you will assume?

_____

_____

13. Is this condition realistic? Explain.

_____

_____

_____

14. On the basis of what you've learned, why would you say that absolute zero is unattainable?

_____

_____

_____

Figure 3 Extrapolating involves using a ruler to extend the line of your graph left and down until it intersects the horizontal axis representing temperature. If these instructions don't match your graph, check with your teacher.

name _____

Table 1		
Temperature (*t*) in °C	Height in cm (*h*)	
	Tube 1	Tube 2

Charles's Law Plot

Height of air column (cm)

Temperature (°C)

10B AN AQUANAUT'S WORLD
Predicting the Production of Oxygen

name _____

section _____   date _____

About 60 feet down on the sandy floor of the Florida Keys by a coral reef rests a yellow metal structure. It isn't a sunken ship or a submarine—it's an underwater laboratory.

Aquarius is one of the few underwater laboratories on Earth dedicated to scientific pursuits. The scientists who work there—called *aquanauts*—live at higher pressures, spending long amounts of time exploring the ocean floor. They don't decompress until their mission is done.

Living and working underwater is similar to living and working in space. There are many challenges to operating in such an environment. Air is supplied to the laboratory by a surface buoy that houses a compressor. The divers use and recharge their air tanks during missions to explore for up to 8 hours. A room in Aquarius maintains pressure to match that of the ocean so that a moon pool can be used to easily enter the marine environment. Life and work at Aquarius is all about two things that you'll explore in this lab—pressure and oxygen.

In 1808 Joseph L. Gay-Lussac formulated the law of combining volumes. He said that under equivalent conditions, the ratio of the volumes of reacting gases and their gaseous products can be expressed in small whole numbers. Although he did not know it at the time, the ratios of the small whole numbers are the same ratios that are expressed as coefficients of balanced equations.

This law of combining volumes later led Amedeo Avogadro to propose the following principle: under equivalent conditions, equal volumes of gases contain the same number of molecules. Later experiments determined just how many molecules were in a given volume. At STP, a volume of 22.4 L contains 6.022×10^{23} molecules, or 1 mole, of a gas. For this reason, 22.4 L is called the *molar volume of a gas*.

In this experiment, you will predict the mass of oxygen gas generated in a reaction. Then you will compare this experimental value to a theoretical value to determine your percent error.

Objectives

✓ Measure the mass and volume of oxygen produced in a chemical reaction.

✓ Calculate the molar mass of oxygen, using the mass and volume of the oxygen produced in a chemical reaction.

✓ Compare the experimental value for molar mass to a theoretical value (from a balanced equation) to determine a percent error.

Equipment

laboratory scale (accurate to 0.01 g)

laboratory thermometer (accurate to 0.1 °C)

barometer

Erlenmeyer flask, 500 mL

beaker, 600 mL

graduated cylinder, 250 mL

graduated cylinder, 25 mL

test tube, large

test tube rack

pinchcock clamp

spatula

tubing, glass and rubber

weighing paper

rubber stoppers, 1-hole and 2-hole

3% hydrogen peroxide (H_2O_2)

manganese dioxide (MnO_2)

Figure 1 Living and working underwater is a bit like being an astronaut! Notice the aquanauts in the cupola of Aquarius.

PROCEDURE

Setting Up

❶ Using the barometer, determine and record today's atmospheric pressure to the nearest 1 torr in Table 1.

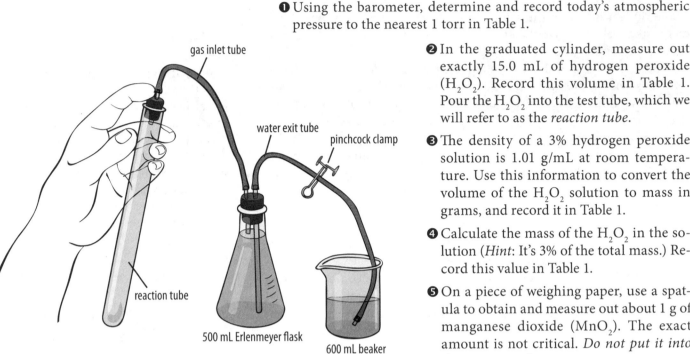

gas inlet tube

water exit tube

pinchcock clamp

reaction tube

500 mL Erlenmeyer flask

600 mL beaker

Figure 2 This is the apparatus to generate oxygen. Use the labels to help you get set up.

❷ In the graduated cylinder, measure out exactly 15.0 mL of hydrogen peroxide (H_2O_2). Record this volume in Table 1. Pour the H_2O_2 into the test tube, which we will refer to as the *reaction tube*.

❸ The density of a 3% hydrogen peroxide solution is 1.01 g/mL at room temperature. Use this information to convert the volume of the H_2O_2 solution to mass in grams, and record it in Table 1.

❹ Calculate the mass of the H_2O_2 in the solution (*Hint*: It's 3% of the total mass.) Record this value in Table 1.

❺ On a piece of weighing paper, use a spatula to obtain and measure out about 1 g of manganese dioxide (MnO_2). The exact amount is not critical. *Do not put it into the reaction tube yet.*

1. The manganese dioxide isn't actually going to react with the hydrogen peroxide. It is speeding up the reaction in which H_2O_2 releases oxygen. What kind of substance is MnO_2 in this reaction?

_____

_____

2. In this reaction, you will be using hydrogen peroxide in the presence of manganese dioxide to produce oxygen gas and water. Write the balanced chemical equation for this reaction, showing where all these chemicals and conditions fit in.

_____

3. What kind of chemical reaction is this?

_____

4. Now make your prediction about how much oxygen gas the reaction would generate at STP. Use the balanced reaction you wrote in Question 2 to find the volume of oxygen produced at STP to the nearest 1 mL. Show your work in the margin if needed.

_____

❻ Assemble the rest of the setup as shown in Figure 2. Fill the 500 mL Erlenmeyer flask with water to just below the neck. Make sure that the bottom end of the reaction side glass tube is about ¼ in. below the rubber stopper. Check to see that the water exit side glass tube is ¼ in. above the bottom of the flask. Keep the water exit tubing clamped with the pinchcock to keep water from running out. Wet the rubber stopper before you insert it in the flask's mouth to improve the seal.

❼ Ask your teacher to check your setup.

Whew! Now you're done setting up!

No Leaks or Bubbles!

The idea of this part of the procedure is to make sure that the setup you just assembled is watertight and that the pressures in the setup are balanced. *It is important that there be no bubbles in the water exit tube.*

❶ Place about 100 mL of water in the 600 mL beaker.

❷ Disconnect the reaction tube by removing the stopper with the tube attached, and remove the pinchcock clamp from the water exit tube.

❸ Tip the flask about 90° to the right so that water can flow through the water exit tube to produce a siphon. The water will not siphon if there is a leak (see Figure 3).

❹ When the water exit tube has filled with water, set the flask down. At this point water should continue siphoning from the flask into the beaker. Stop the siphoning by clamping the water exit tube with the pinchcock.

❺ Now siphon the water back into the flask so that the water level in the flask is just below the reaction side inlet tube. To do this, raise the beaker above the water level in the flask and remove the clamp (see Figure 4).

name _____

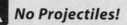

⚠ **No Projectiles!**

Point the reaction tube away from people while observing the reaction as much as possible, just in case the rubber stopper comes loose. We don't want any projectiles!

Figure 3 Siphoning water from the flask to the beaker to fill the tube with water

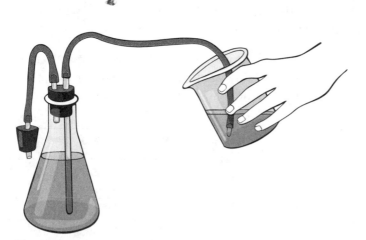

Figure 4 Siphon water from the beaker to the flask until the water level is just below the gas inlet tube.

❻ As soon as the flask fills to the desired level, replace the clamp and put the beaker back on the desk.

❼ Wet the reaction tube stopper and insert it into the mouth of the test tube. Confirm that both stoppers are snug.

❽ Remove the clamp. The water level in the flask will fall slightly. After this change, the water level should remain at the new position.

❾ Equalize the air pressure in the flask with that of the atmosphere by lifting the beaker so that its water level is even with the water level in the flask. Replace the clamp while the water levels are matched (see Figure 5). Once you've clamped the tube, you can put the beaker back on the table.

5. Why is it important that there be no leaks or bubbles in your setup and that the air pressure in the flask be equal to atmospheric pressure?

_____

_____

_____

_____

Figure 5 Equalize the pressure in the tubes by lining up the water levels in the Erlenmeyer flask and the beaker. Put on the pinchcock clamp when water levels are equal.

❿ Empty and dry the beaker and return it to the assembly.

Making Oxygen

❶ Remove the stopper from the reaction tube and pour the manganese dioxide into the hydrogen peroxide solution. Quickly restopper the tube and remove the clamp. Hold the reaction tube vertically near the top. With one finger, hold the stopper firmly in place. Swirl the tube to speed up the reaction. Every few seconds, give the tube another swirl.

6. Record anything that you observe during the reaction, including changes in the reaction mixture, the space of air over the water in the flask, and the amount of water in the beaker.

_____

_____

_____

_____

_____

_____

7. Are the reaction conditions for your production of oxygen gas STP conditions? Explain.

_____

_____

_____

_____

_____

name _____

What Is STP?
Did you forget what STP is? Check page 257 in your textbook.

❷ After about 10 minutes, very little water should be coming out of the water exit tube. Consider the reaction finished at this point even though the mixture in the reaction tube may still be bubbling slightly.

8. The volume of water in the beaker represents the volume of displaced water. What else does this volume equal?

_____

_____

❸ Lift the beaker so that its water level matches the water level in the flask. Clamp the water exit tube with the pinchcock. This final step equalizes the air pressure in the flask. *Immediately remove the stopper from the reaction tube so that it doesn't pop out under pressure!*

❹ Pour the water from the beaker into the large graduated cylinder, and determine its volume to the nearest 1.00 mL. Record the result in Table 1.

❺ Measure the temperature of the water in the graduated cylinder to the nearest 0.1 °C. Convert the result to kelvins and record both temperatures in Table 1.

9. Why do you need to take the temperature of the water?

_____

_____

_____

10. Look back at Question 2. Where did the oxygen go after the hydrogen peroxide began to react?

_____

_____

_____

11. Where did the water go after the H_2O_2 reacted?

_____

12. Where did the MnO_2 go after the H_2O_2 reacted?

_____

13. Use Table 10-4 on page 263 of your textbook to obtain the partial pressure of the water vapor that is present along with the oxygen in the flask. Use the temperature that you determined in step ❺, interpolating between table entries if necessary.

_____

14. Use the current atmospheric pressure and the partial pressure of water vapor to calculate the partial pressure of oxygen. You can show your work in the margin if needed. Round your result to the nearest 1 torr. This is your P_1.

_____

15. What is the temperature of the oxygen in kelvins?

_____

So far you have used your measurements to determine the initial pressure (P_1), volume (V_1), and temperature (T_1) of the oxygen gas.

16. Now use the appropriate gas law to find the volume of the oxygen if the conditions were changed to STP. Show your work in the margin if needed. Round your result to the nearest 1 mL.

_____

17. Look back at your predicted value for the volume of oxygen gas generated at STP from the decomposition of H_2O_2 (Question 4). Do a percent error calculation to compare your experimental results and the theoretical value.

_____

18. Explain possible causes for quantities of oxygen smaller and larger than predicted.

_____

_____

_____

_____

_____

_____

_____

_____

19. Not only was your experiment today not at STP; the aquanaut's world isn't at STP either! In fact, if these research scientists don't consider the pressure and temperature conditions, it could cost them their lives. How do you think aquanauts need to adjust for these conditions?

_____

_____

_____

_____

_____

name _____

The Bends

When divers surface too quickly after a deep dive, bubbles can develop in their bloodstream, causing extreme pain and sometimes even death. This experience isn't limited to divers. Astronauts and pilots can experience the bends, also called *decompression sickness*. It's all about pressure and gases!

Table 1	
Atmospheric pressure (torr)	
Volume of 3% H_2O_2 solution	
Mass of H_2O_2 solution	
Mass of H_2O_2	
Volume of water from beaker (mL) (V_1 of oxygen)	
Temperature of water from beaker (°C) (t_1 of oxygen)	
Temperature of water from beaker (K) (T_1 of oxygen)	

11   SOLIDS AND LIQUIDS

11A FORCES OF NATURE
Exploring Intermolecular Forces in Liquids

name _____

section _____   date _____

It is wintertime in the woods of Colorado. A blanket of snow covers the ice on a pond. Wait—there's a mound in the middle of the pond. It must be a beaver lodge.

Beavers will spend all winter without breathing the air outside their lodges since they have underwater front doors. They fill their time swimming under the ice and lounging in their lodges. In the still winter air, you noiselessly walk up to the mound over freshly fallen snow and hear the sounds of beavers gnawing on bark from their winter stash of branches.

Then on the perimeter of the pond you see a wolverine! You realize with relief that this predator can't get to the beavers, who are protected by their lodge and the shield of ice that floats over the pond.

Why does ice float like this? If water behaved like most liquids, the ice would be denser, making it sink to the bottom of the pond. The intermolecular forces in water—London dispersion forces, dipole-dipole forces, and, most of all, hydrogen bonds—make ice less dense than water, causing it to float. Because of this, beavers have a nice winter vacation under the ice!

In this lab, you will be investigating the intermolecular forces in four liquids—water, acetone (CH_3COCH_3), ethanol (CH_3CH_2OH), and mineral oil. (Mineral oil is a mixture of chemicals, but they are mostly long molecules that contain only carbon and hydrogen. These molecules are usually chains with 15–40 carbons in them. We'll use a 15-carbon molecule as our model for the behavior of mineral oil.) The four liquids have different properties because they are made of molecules containing different arrangements of atoms. Let's see how intermolecular forces affect a liquid's density, viscosity, solubility, surface tension, and ease of evaporation.

Objectives

✓ Compare the viscosity, surface tension, solubility, and volatility of four liquids.

✓ Relate viscosity, surface tension, solubility, and volatility to the polarity of liquid molecules.

✓ Relate viscosity, surface tension, solubility, and volatility to the molecular mass of molecules.

✓ Use data to explain how intermolecular forces affect the characteristics of liquids.

Equipment

marbles (4)
rubber stoppers without holes (4)
stopwatch
beakers, 10 mL (4)
beaker, 100 mL
eyedroppers or pipets (4)
watch glass
pennies (4)
test tubes, large (4)
test tubes, small (3)
food coloring
Vernier LabQuest® or LabQuest 2®
Vernier Stainless Steel Temperature Probe
filter paper
masking tape
water (20 mL)
acetone (20 mL)
ethanol (20 mL)
mineral oil (20 mL)

Figure 1 Beavers spend all winter under a shield of ice that floats because of intermolecular forces.

PROCEDURE

Making Predictions

Before you get started, let's think about the substances that you will be working with. Notice their Lewis structures on the next page. Mineral oil is represented by pentadecane, a 15-carbon molecule.

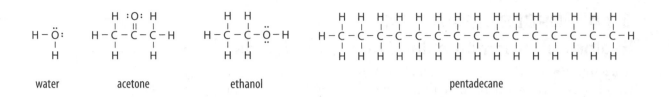

water   acetone   ethanol   pentadecane

1. Which of the four substances are polar?

_____

Dipole moments, a measure of polarity, can be measured for a molecule and assigned a number. They are measured in a unit called the *debye (D)*, defined as the measure of charge and the distance that separates areas of charge. The dipole moments for pure samples of the four liquids are provided in the margin box.

2. Using the given dipole moment measurements, which substance is the most polar?

_____

3. Which molecule has the highest molecular weight? Which one has the lowest?

_____

_____

4. How do you think the weight of the molecule will affect the way it responds to intermolecular forces?

_____

_____

_____

Now let's think about the polarity and the molecular weight of acetone. You will make some predictions about how acetone will compare to the other three liquids.

Viscosity, which is a liquid's resistance to flow, is measured in Pa · s, or pascal-seconds. The pascal is a unit of pressure, and pascal-seconds are related to the rate of flow of a liquid. The higher the viscosity value, the thicker and more resistant to flow the liquid will be. Viscosity is a form of cohesion.

5. With 4 being the highest and 1 being the lowest, predict acetone's viscosity compared to the other three liquids.

_____

6. With 4 being the highest and 1 being the lowest, predict acetone's surface tension compared to the other three liquids.

_____

7. Do you think acetone will mix with water?

_____

Dipole Moment Data

water: 1.85 D

acetone: 2.91 D

ethanol: 1.69 D

pentadecane: 0 D

The tendency of a liquid to evaporate into a gas is called its *volatility*. Liquids with low vapor pressures and low boiling points are extremely volatile.

8. With 4 being the highest and 1 being the lowest, predict acetone's volatility compared to the other four liquids.

_____

Now, let's look at how these intermolecular forces affect how these liquids behave. You can do each of the following parts of this lab in any order, so if another group is using something you need, skip to another part of the procedure.

Viscosity

❶ Notice that there is a marble at the bottom of each of the four large, labeled, stoppered test tubes. Swirl the contents of each test tube.

9. Which liquid do you think is the most viscous?

_____

❷ Now let's find out if you're right. Give the stopwatch to one person designated from your group to use it.

❸ One at a time, invert each tube so that the marble settles to the stoppered end of the test tube.

❹ Invert each tube again, starting the stopwatch as soon as the test tube is in the upright position. Stop the stopwatch as soon as the marble reaches the bottom of the test tube.

❺ Do three trials for each liquid, recording your results in Table 1 on the next page.

❻ Average your trials to find one value for the time of the marble's fall for each liquid. Record this data in Table 1.

10. Why should you do more than one trial for each liquid?

_____

_____

_____

11. In which liquid did the marble take the longest to fall? How does this relate to viscosity? Did this follow your prediction?

_____

_____

_____

name _____

Figure 2 Farmers boiling maple sap to make maple syrup use a hydrometer to tell when the sap has become syrup. The viscosity of the fluid changes during this process.

12. Explain why you think this liquid was most viscous.

_____

_____

_____

_____

13. How do intermolecular forces affect viscosity?

_____

_____

_____

Consider the viscosities of pure samples of the four liquids at room temperature provided in the margin box.

14. How do these values of viscosity relate to what you observed?

_____

_____

_____

Viscosity Data

water: 1.002 mPa · s

acetone: 0.3311 mPa · s

ethanol: 1.114 mPa · s

pentadecane: 2.863 mPa · s

15. Evaluate your prediction of acetone's viscosity.

_____

_____

_____

Table 1 Time of the Marble's Fall (s)				
	Trial 1	Trial 2	Trial 3	Average
In water				
In acetone				
In ethanol				
In mineral oil				

Surface Tension

❶ Fill four 10 mL beakers with fresh samples of each of the four liquids; label each one. You will need a dropper or pipet for each of the four liquids.

❷ Wash four pennies with detergent, and then dry them. Put a large watch glass on top of your lab bench, and put a paper towel on it. Put four pennies on the paper towel. Label the paper towel to show which penny is used for which liquid.

16. How do you think the surface tension of a liquid relates to the number of drops that you could fit on a penny?

_____

_____

name _____

❸ Using the pipet, add drops of each liquid to a penny until the liquid overflows onto the paper towel. Keep a careful count of the drops and record them in Table 2 below. Do this step as quickly as possible since some of the liquids evaporate fairly rapidly.

❹ Clean all four pennies well, and then dry them. Repeat step ❸ a second time for all four liquids and record your results in Table 2.

❺ Average your results; record this data in Table 2.

Figure 3 Testing the surface tension of the liquids

17. Which liquid has the highest surface tension? Why do you think this is so?

_____

_____

_____

_____

18. How do intermolecular forces affect surface tension?

_____

_____

19. Evaluate your prediction of acetone's surface tension.

_____

_____

_____

Table 2			
	# of drops to cover a penny Trial 1	# of drops to cover a penny Trial 2	Average # of drops to cover a penny
Water			
Acetone			
Ethanol			
Mineral oil			

Solubility

❶ Fill three small test tubes halfway, one with acetone, another with ethanol, and the last with mineral oil. Label your test tubes.

❷ Fill a 100 mL beaker three-quarters full with water. Add a few drops of food coloring of your choice.

❸ Add the colored water to the three test tubes until they are almost full.

20. What do you observe about the three liquids?

_____

_____

21. Explain why your liquids behaved the way they did on the basis of intermolecular forces. (*Hint*: See Table 11-2 on page 287 of your textbook.)

_____

_____

_____

_____

_____

When two liquids mix together, or one dissolves in the other, they are said to be *miscible*.

22. How do intermolecular forces relate to miscibility?

_____

_____

_____

Oil on Water

How do you think the miscibility of your liquids relates to cleaning up an oil spill?

23. Evaluate your prediction of acetone's ability to dissolve in water.

_____

_____

_____

Volatility

❶ Now get the Vernier LabQuest or LabQuest 2 and plug the Stainless Steel Temperature Probe into the **CH 1** port.

❷ Turn the LabQuest on. Tap the **Duration** box (**Length** on the original LabQuest) to the right of the meter display and enter **180** (3 minutes). Confirm that the unit box is set to **s** (seconds). If it isn't, tap the down-arrow next to the unit box and set the unit to **s**. Tap **OK**.

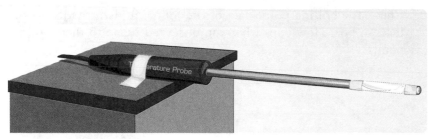

Figure 4 Setup for testing the volatility of the liquids

❸ Wrap a single layer of filter paper around the end of the temperature probe and secure it with tape. Trim or tear off any excess.

❹ Dip the tip covered in filter paper in one of the four liquids until the paper is saturated. Take the probe out of the beaker, touching the probe to the inside of the beaker to get rid of any drips.

❺ Tape the probe onto the edge of the lab bench as shown in Figure 4. Press the LabQuest **Collect** button. Watch the temperature graph develop over time.

❻ The LabQuest will automatically stop after 3 minutes. (If you need to stop early for some reason, press the **Collect** button again.) Tap **Analyze** and then **Statistics**. Tap the checkbox next to **Temperature**. A statistics box will appear next to the graph.

❼ Locate the values next to **max** and **min** and subtract them. The result represents the temperature change caused by the evaporating liquid. Record this value in Table 3 in the margin.

❽ Remove the filter paper and wipe the probe with a paper towel. Repeat steps ❸ through ❼ for the other three liquids, recording the temperature changes in Table 3. Make sure that you change the filter paper each time! When you are ready to collect new data for a new liquid, press the **Collect** button. When the LabQuest asks you what to do with the previous data, tap **Discard**.

24. Why did the temperature drop noticeably for some samples over time?

_____

_____

25. Using your data, which liquid did you observe to evaporate the most quickly? How do you know?

_____

_____

_____

> ### Testing Your Liquids
>
> If you have any liquid left in the 10 mL beakers from the surface tension test, you may use that, or you can get about 5 mL of liquid in the same beakers.

Table 3	
	Change (°C)
Water	
Acetone	
Ethanol	
Mineral oil	

Figure 5 During the process of boiling down sap to make maple syrup, the surface of the sap can become quite turbulent. When this happens, farmers put a pat of butter on the sap to break up the turbulence, reducing its volatility.

Boiling Point Data

water: 100 °C

acetone: 56–57 °C

ethanol: 78.5 °C

pentadecane: 212.41 °C

26. Check the boiling point data of the four liquids provided in the margin box. How does what you observed relate to their boiling points?

_____

_____

_____

27. How do intermolecular forces affect volatility?

_____

_____

28. Evaluate your prediction of acetone's volatility.

_____

_____

29. Look back at the Lewis structures of the four liquids. What properties of these molecules affected their viscosity, surface tension, solubility, and volatility?

_____

_____

_____

_____

Pulling It All Together

Using the data that you have been given in this lab and the experimentation that you have done, you will now rank the properties of the four liquids. Record your results in Table 4 on the facing page.

❶ Rank the polarity of all four liquids, with 4 being the highest and 1 being the lowest.

❷ Rank the molecular weight of all four liquids, with 1 being the highest and 4 being the lowest. This scale has been reversed because molecular weight and the influence of intermolecular forces are inversely related.

❸ Rank the viscosity of all four liquids, with 1 representing the most resistance to flow and 4 the least resistance to flow.

❹ Rank the surface tension of all four liquids, with 4 being the highest and 1 being the lowest.

❺ If the liquid is miscible in water, assign a score of 4. If it is not, assign a score of 0. Assign water a score of 4.

❻ Rank the volatility of all four liquids, with 1 being the least volatile (having the highest boiling point) and 4 being the most volatile (having the lowest boiling point).

❼ Add up your scores.

30. What kind of scores do the polar molecules have? How does this compare with nonpolar molecules?

name _____

_____

_____

31. How do these scores relate to what you observed about water and acetone?

_____

_____

32. How do these scores relate to how ethanol compares with water and acetone?

_____

_____

33. How do these scores relate to what you observed about mineral oil?

_____

_____

_____

34. Relate all these comparisons to the types of intermolecular forces these liquids experience.

_____

_____

_____

_____

Table 4 Ranking the Four Liquids				
	Water	Acetone	Ethanol	Mineral oil
Polarity				
Molecular weight				
Viscosity				
Surface tension				
Miscibility				
Volatility				
Sum of scores				

11B CRACKING THE CRYSTAL
Inquiring into Geology with Chemistry

name _____

section _____ date _____

The largest acid lake in the world, Kawah Ijen, is located in a string of volcanoes in Indonesia, one of which is the famous Krakatoa. This lake contains sulfuric acid with the potency of a car battery. No swimming here! If you even get close, you could be blasted by sulfuric acid gases from nearby volcanic vents.

Indonesian miners eke out a living in this alien landscape by gathering sulfur from naturally occurring deposits along the shores of this unearthly turquoise-colored lake. This sulfur grows in characteristic crystals that can be predicted by—you guessed it—chemistry. The miners sell the sulfur, some of it carved into statues and figures.

You've spent some time in your textbook learning how crystal shapes affect the formation of minerals. Now you get to explore minerals on your own, looking at some real minerals and thinking about what is happening at the atomic level to produce the crystals that you hold in your hand.

> ### Objectives
> ✓ Observe and identify the crystal structures of certain minerals.
> ✓ Identify types of crystals.
> ✓ Relate the molecular and ionic structure of compounds to their crystal shape.

> ### Equipment
> minerals
> magnifying glass
> stereomicroscope
> computer with Internet access

Figure 1 Though the work is dangerous, men mine the shores of a crater lake for sulfur crystals to make a living.

PROCEDURE

In this lab, you will design your own procedure! Your goal is this: *To explain the crystal shapes of different minerals using their chemical crystal structure.* As you do, consider the following:

❶ Make sure that you are thinking about minerals and not rocks. Minerals are more often pure substances chemically.

❷ Think about what kind of chemical you are dealing with: an atomic crystal, a covalent molecular crystal, a covalent network crystal, an ionic crystal, or a metallic crystal.

❸ Try to determine the formula for the crystal that you are examining. Sketch the crystal in the space provided in Table 1, identifying the atoms in your formula unit somehow.

❹ Some minerals may be allotropes. Watch out for these!

❺ Try to get an actual sample. If you can't, harness the power of the Internet to look at lots of different pictures of your mineral.

❻ If you have a sample, examine it with a magnifying glass or a stereo-microscope. If you are working with digital pictures of minerals, zoom in to see lots of detail.

❼ Use Table 1 to record any observations or notes on the minerals you examine.

Think About It

1. Sulfur is an example of an atomic crystal that has many allotropes. In its solid state, it can appear in granular deposits or as an ortho-rhombic crystal. The number of sulfur atoms that form rings in the formula unit of these crystals can range from 6 to as many as 20. Why do you think sulfur forms such a wide range of crystals?

_____

_____

_____

_____

_____

_____

_____

2. What do you think determines the form that sulfur will take?

_____

_____

_____

_____

_____

_____

_____

3. One of the most common forms of sulfur is cyclooctasulfur, S_8. In nature, it forms crystals with a rhombohedral shape. Using the photograph in Figure 2, write a paragraph that relates the shape of the formula unit to its crystal shape.

name _____

_____

_____

_____

_____

_____

_____

4. The opener to this lab shows how people are mining sulfur from the lake in Indonesia. Why is it important to investigate crystals like sulfur and their properties?

_____

_____

_____

_____

_____

_____

_____

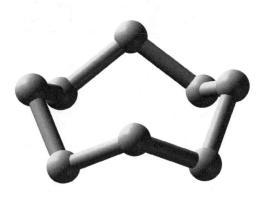

Figure 2 Formula unit of cyclooctasulfur (top); sample of rhombohedral sulfur (bottom)

YOUR PLAN

_____

_____

_____

_____

_____

_____

_____

_____

_____

_____

YOUR FINDINGS

Table 1		
Mineral	Observations	Sketches

12 SOLUTIONS

12A THE BEACH IS CLOSED
Eutrophication and Blooming Water

name _____

section _____   date _____

The beach is closed at Galveston, Texas—not that anyone would want to swim there anyway. A red flush in the water makes it look like toxic soup. Algae sometimes turn the water red, earning it the title "red tide." This condition can be hazardous both to sea life and people, irritating the skin and causing sickness and infections.

Though the scenario described above is sometimes a naturally occurring phenomenon, that's not always the case. Fertilizers used in farming can get washed into streams, lakes, and ultimately the ocean. Nitrogen and phosphorus locked inside chemical compounds are two of the most important ingredients in fertilizers. This is why fertilizers are used on most of the world's food crops. So you could say that without nitrogen and phosphorus, you wouldn't be eating a salad, a hamburger, or anything else for lunch. But what happens when these two elements become concentrated in a closed system? Can a lot of nitrogen and phosphorus in the environment actually be a bad thing?

Oxygen is another element that is vital for life. When too much nitrogen and phosphorus enter a body of water, algae grow at an incredible rate, and the levels of oxygen in the water change. This process is known as *eutrophication*, and the fast growth rate of algae is called an *algal bloom*. At first, fish and other organisms enjoy the algal smorgasbord. But the algae's fast growth rate leads to a fast death rate. As the algae die, bacteria decompose them. These bacteria use oxygen as they break down the dead algae, eventually using up the oxygen in the water and suffocating the fish.

Oxygen gets added back into the water when it rains, each raindrop mixing a little bit of atmospheric oxygen into the water. Plants growing along the bank also contribute oxygen to the water. But if you've ever seen a pond covered in green scum, then you've seen a pond that needs more than a good rain storm. Is there any way to reverse a eutrophic body of water? You'll find out as you do this lab exploring the substances dissolved in eutrophic water.

Objectives

✓ Observe the effects of nitrogen and phosphorus from fertilizer on a sample of pond water.

✓ Relate the levels of oxygen, pH, and temperature to eutrophication.

✓ Recommend ways to restore the biological and chemical balance to a eutrophic pond.

Equipment

Vernier LabQuest® or LabQuest® 2

Vernier Stainless Steel Temperature Probe

Vernier pH Sensor

Vernier Dissolved Oxygen Probe

laboratory scale (accurate to 0.01 g)

ring stand and ring

clay triangle

funnel, large

beakers, 250 mL (6)

glass stirring rod

watch glass, large

watch glasses, medium (3)

wash bottle

pond water (approximately 300 mL)

6 g of 10-10-10 fertilizer

wax pencil or tape and a felt-tip marker

3 pieces of filter paper

paper towels

weighing paper

Figure 1 The biology and chemistry of this lake are unbalanced. A lake should not be this green!

PROCEDURE

Setting Up

❶ Label three beakers A, B, and C. Weigh each empty beaker and record its initial mass to the nearest 0.01 g in Table 1.

❷ Fill each beaker with about 100 mL of pond water.

❸ Weigh each beaker with pond water, and record its final mass in Table 1.

1. Why do you think mass will be more important than volume during this lab? (*Hint*: Liquid solutions are usually measured by volume.)

_____

_____

_____

_____

Beaker A will be the control beaker; you won't be adding anything else to this beaker.

❹ On a piece of weighing paper, measure out 2.0 g of fertilizer. Add this to Beaker B and stir well.

❺ Weigh out 4.0 g of fertilizer on a piece of weighing paper, and add it to Beaker C and stir well.

Fertilizer is a mixture of nitrates, ammonium sulfate, ammonium phosphate, potassium magnesium sulfate, potassium chloride, boron compounds, iron compounds, manganese compounds, and sand. What a concoction! Runoff water from farm fields can be laden with chemicals from fertilizers.

2. Considering the introduction to this lab, how do you think adding fertilizer will affect your pond water?

_____

_____

_____

_____

_____

3. Suggest ways to reduce the amount of fertilizer that gets into our streams, rivers, and lakes.

_____

_____

_____

_____

Where Does Fertilizer Come From?

For a look at where fertilizer comes from, see pages 393–94 from Chapter 15 in your textbook. You'll learn about Fritz Haber, the man behind the manufacture of artificial fertilizer.

Figure 2 In the last 30 years, the United States has doubled its corn production, all because of the improving science of fertilizers.

name _____

❻ Plug the Stainless Steel Temperature Probe into the **CH 1** port of the LabQuest.

❼ Plug the pH Sensor into the **CH 2** port. *Be very careful with this probe because the tip is made of thin glass and is very fragile.*

❽ Plug the Dissolved Oxygen Probe into the **CH 3** port. Turn on the LabQuest. You must keep this probe submerged in water and attached to the LabQuest at all times. The Dissolved Oxygen Probe will need 10 minutes to warm up.

Measuring Starting Temperature

Now you need to take initial readings of your pond water.

❶ Dip the tip of the Stainless Steel Temperature Probe into Beaker A.

❷ Repeat step ❶ for the other two beakers and record the initial temperature of each to the nearest 0.1°C in Table 1.

4. What did you observe in your temperature readings for the three beakers?

_____

_____

Measuring Starting pH

You will now measure the pH of the pond water. The pH scale ranges from 1 to 14, with a pH of 7 being a neutral solution. Solutions with a pH less than 7 are acidic, and solutions with a pH greater than 7 are basic.

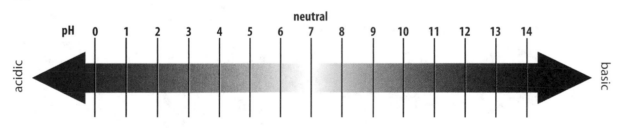

Figure 3 The pH scale

5. Predict whether the pH of the water in each beaker will be acidic, neutral, or basic. You may need to do a little research to answer this question.

_____

_____

_____

❸ Now, disconnect the Stainless Steel Temperature Probe and plug the pH Sensor into the **CH1** port.

Handle with Care

Be very careful when handling the pH probe because it is made of thin glass and is very fragile.

❹ Thoroughly rinse the tip of the pH probe over a sink with a wash bottle of distilled water. Dip the tip of the sensor in Beaker A and press the **Collect** button. Record the initial pH in Table 1.

❺ Repeat step ❹ for the other two beakers.

6. What did you observe in your pH readings for the three beakers?

_____

_____

Measuring Starting O₂ Levels

❶ Dip the tip of the Dissolved Oxygen Probe in Beaker A and stir gently while watching the LabQuest display. Keep the probe moving and wait for the display to settle to a fairly consistent value. Record what you consider a representative initial oxygen level value in Table 1.

❷ Repeat step ❶ for the other two beakers. Thoroughly rinse the probe tip before storing it.

7. What did you observe in the oxygen level readings for the three beakers?

_____

_____

❸ Cover the three beakers with a medium-sized watch glass. Place them near a window but *not* in direct sun or in a room that has a fluorescent light on for at least 10 hours each day. Leave the beakers there for the next 3 days.

8. Why are warmth, light, and time important for the pond water?

_____

_____

Measuring Final Levels

After 3 days, the algae—and possibly other things—in the pond water should be growing.

9. What observations can you make of each beaker, such as color and clarity of the water, particles or bubbles in the water, smell, and so on?

_____

_____

_____

10. Beakers B and C should be slightly heavier than Beaker A for a reason other than that it contains more algae. What is the reason? (*Hint*: Think back to when you first set up the beakers.)

_____

_____

❶ Measure the temperature, pH, and amount of dissolved oxygen in each beaker using the procedures outlined earlier. Record these final measurements in Table 1.

11. Normal oxygen levels in a pond will vary during the year, but a healthy level is between 7 and 12 mg/L. What happened to the oxygen levels in the three beakers? Do you think a fish would be happy to live in any one of them?

_____

_____

_____

12. The photosynthesis of algae makes pond water more acidic. Does a comparison of your initial and final pH measurements of Beakers B and C agree with this? Explain.

_____

_____

name _____

Filtering the Pond Water

❶ Obtain a piece of large filter paper and a large watch glass in which to place the paper. Weigh them together.

13. What is their combined weight?

_____

❷ In order to filter Beakers A, B, and C, assemble a ring stand, ring, three 250 mL beakers, a clay triangle, and large funnel as shown in Figure 4.

❸ *This step could be messy, so do it slowly.* Pour Beaker A carefully into the funnel and let the water drip into the empty beaker. Once all the water has passed through the filter paper, you should be left with a piece of filter paper full of sludge.

14. Describe the color of the water from Beaker A.

_____

_____

Figure 4 Setup for filtering the pond water

❹ Remove the filter paper from the funnel and place it on several layers of paper towels, being careful not to lose any of the sludge. Wait 1 minute to let the paper towels soak some of the water out of the filter paper. You may have to change paper towels if they become saturated.

❺ Place the filter paper with the sludge (but not the paper towels) on the watch glass. Record the mass of the sludge in Table 1. (Remember to subtract the weight of the filter paper and watch glass that you determined in step ❶ above.)

❻ Discard the filter paper with sludge and pour the pond water down the sink with plenty of running water. Rinse and dry the container, funnel, and dish.

❼ Repeat steps ❸–❻ for Beakers B and C.

15. Describe the color of the water from Beakers B and C.

_____

_____

16. Why is your measure of the mass of sludge not quite accurate?

_____

17. Can you think of at least one way to improve the accuracy?

_____

_____

18. Compare the water color of Beakers B and C with the water color of Beaker A.

_____

_____

Pond water is a solution—the water is a solvent, and everything dissolved in the water is a solute.

19. Calculate the percent by mass of the sludge that you filtered out of each beaker. Make sure to subtract the mass of the empty beakers from the mass of the beakers with pond water in them.

_____

_____

20. Which beaker has the greatest percentage of sludge?

_____

21. What is the relationship between the algae sludge in each beaker and the amount of fertilizer you added?

_____

_____

22. Not only did you have water in your sludge, but you also left sludge in the water! How do you think this affects the percent by mass that you calculated?

_____

_____

23. Can you think of some ways to completely remove all solutes from the water that is left in the beakers so that you can more accurately calculate the percent by mass?

name _____

_____

_____

_____

24. Oxygen levels are typically lower in the summer and higher in the winter. Using this information, what would you say is the relationship between temperature and oxygen levels?

_____

_____

25. Do you think that the temperature of the beakers may have affected oxygen levels? Explain.

_____

_____

26. An ecologist who is trying to reverse the effects of fertilizer in a pond makes only one change to the pond: adding a chemical that will give the water a neutral pH. Do you think this will work? Why or why not?

_____

_____

_____

_____

_____

27. Using what you've learned about oxygen, temperature, pH, and the effects of fertilizer on algae, come up with a plan for how you would return the pond back to normal. Be creative!

_____

_____

_____

_____

_____

_____

_____

Beaker	Mass (g)		Fertilizer added (g)	Temperature (°C)		pH		Dissolved oxygen (mg/L)		Mass of sludge (g)
	Initial	Final		Initial	Final	Initial	Final	Initial	Final	
A			0							
B			2.0							
C			4.0							

Table 1

12B ONE GIANT SOLUTION
Making a Solubility Curve

name _____

section _____   date _____

A mother humpback whale has just arrived off the coast of Hawaii, having traveled the longest migration route of any mammal. She is ready to give birth in the clear, warm waters of the tropics after having spent the summer feeding in the frigid waters of Alaska, where pollock and mackerel thrive. But now she has come to the tropics, though it means she must do without food for several months, so that she can have a warm place for her baby to grow. The clear tropic waters allow her to see predators from far away.

Objectives

✓ Demonstrate how the solubility of a salt varies with temperature.

✓ Plot the solubility curve of a salt on the basis of observed data.

There's another reason humpbacks travel all this way: solubility. You've learned that solubility is the amount of solute that will dissolve in a given amount of solvent to make a saturated solution. Well, the ocean is one giant solution! Pollock and mackerel, as well as the krill, phytoplankton, and algae that these fish feed on, need dissolved oxygen and nutrients to get food. Colder waters are able to hold more oxygen since the solubility of gases increases with decreasing temperature. Other nutrients such as salts are stirred up by deep currents, though their solubility is also affected by the cold polar waters.

In the oceans we can see how solubility varies with different conditions, such as temperature. You will see this for yourself in this lab as you vary the temperature and observe how solids dissolved in a solution respond to these changes.

Equipment

laboratory scale (accurate to 0.01 g)

laboratory burner and lighter

ring stand and ring

wire gauze

beaker, 250 mL

glass stirring rod

graduated cylinder, 10 mL

metric ruler

test tube rack

test tubes, medium (4)

laboratory thermometer

ammonium chloride (NH_4Cl)

masking tape or grease pencil

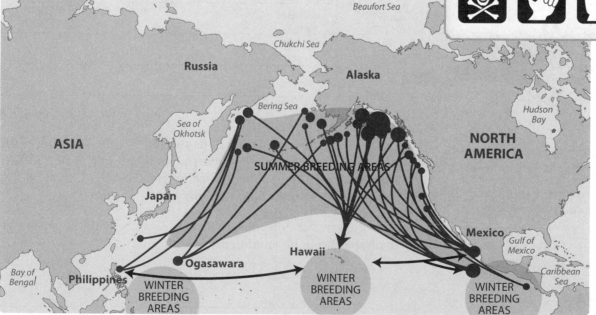

Figure 1 Humpback whales travel north in the summer to feed on fish and krill that are abundant in polar waters. They travel south to tropic waters to give birth, though they must fast for several months to do so.

Squids and Ammonium Chloride

Ammonium chloride is used as a flavoring in cookies, bread, and some types of licorice. It is one of the main ingredients in fertilizers and expectorants used in cough syrups. Giant squids use ammonium chloride solutions in their bodies to maintain a neutral buoyancy in seawater. This makes them horrible to eat!

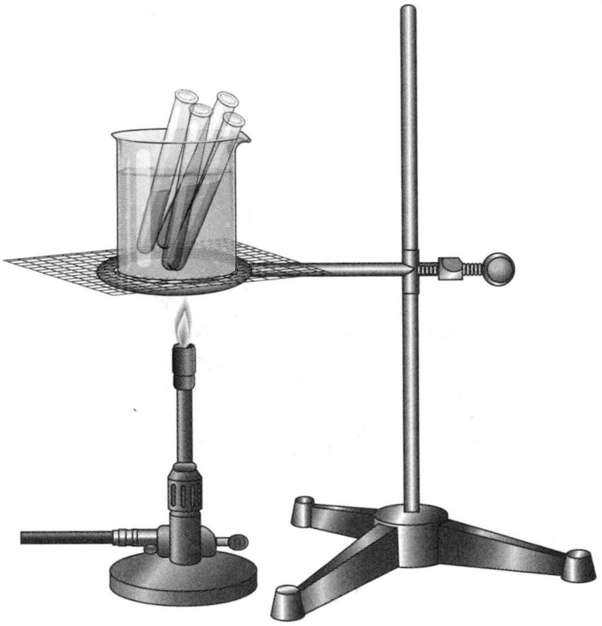

PROCEDURE

Setting Up

❶ Label four medium test tubes as follows: "4.00," "4.50," "5.00," and "5.50." Put these test tubes in a test tube rack.

❷ Add 4.00 g of ammonium chloride to the test tube labeled "4.00." Add 4.50 g, 5.00 g, and 5.50 g of ammonium chloride, adding each mass to its respective test tube.

1. Which sample will dissolve the quickest? Explain.

_____

_____

❸ Add exactly 10.0 mL of water to each test tube.

2. Which tube do you think will form crystals the quickest when cooled?

_____

_____

❹ Set up a hot-water bath, as shown in Figure 2. Make sure that you add enough water (about 150 mL) so that the level in the hot-water bath is higher than the liquid levels in the test tubes when all four test tubes are in the beaker.

❺ Place the four test tubes into the hot-water bath. Do not allow any water from the beaker to get into the test tubes!

3. Why is it important that no water from the hot-water bath be allowed to get into the test tubes?

_____

_____

_____

_____

Figure 2 Setup for testing solubility

Keep It Clean!

Be sure to rinse and dry the stirring rod before putting it into a different solution.

Testing Solubility

❶ When the hot-water bath begins to boil, stir the solutions with the stirring rod to help dissolve the ammonium chloride. When the solute in all four tubes has completely dissolved, turn off the burner. *Note that the bath will stay hot for a while.*

4. Use the kinetic molecular theory to describe why the hot-water bath speeds up the solution process for solids.

_____

_____

_____

❷ Using a test tube holder, remove test tube "5.50" from the water bath and place it in the test tube rack. Place a thermometer into the test tube and allow the solution to cool.

❸ When crystals start forming in the liquid, record the temperature in the Trial 1 column of Table 1. Double-check this temperature by reheating the test tube just enough to dissolve the solute again. Record this second reading in the Trial 2 column of Table 1.

❹ Repeat steps ❷ and ❸ for the solutions containing 5.00, 4.50, and 4.00 g of ammonium chloride.

5. Which tube formed crystals the quickest? How did this compare with your prediction in Question 2?

_____

_____

❺ Plot your solubility data from Table 1 in the graphing area on the next page.

❻ Draw a smooth curve connecting the points. Using a ruler, extrapolate the curve to the edges of the graph.

6. Determine the solubility of ammonium chloride (in g/10.0 mL H_2O) at 60 °C from your solubility curve.

_____

7. Obtain the accepted value for the solubility of ammonium chloride from your teacher. Calculate your percent error. Show your work in the margin if needed.

_____

8. Describe how the shape of the solubility curve would change, if at all, if your thermometer readings were all 4.5 °C lower than what you measured.

_____

_____

_____

9. You have learned that the solubilities of gases decrease with increasing temperature. Predict how a solubility curve of a gas would look compared to one for a solid.

_____

_____

_____

name _____

Cooling and Recooling

If the temperatures for the first and second crystallizations differ by more than a few degrees, carefully repeat the reheating and recooling process.

Speeding Up the Crystals!

You may need an ice-water bath to speed up the crystallization of the 4.00 g sample.

10. In the introduction we noted that the ocean is one giant solution that humpback whales rely on. The other solution that these whales rely on is their blood. How are the solutions of ocean water and blood similar? How are they different?

_____

_____

_____

_____

_____

_____

_____

_____

Table 1		
Mass of NH$_4$Cl (g)	Temperature for crystallization (°C)	
	Trial 1	Trial 2
5.50		
5.00		
4.50		
4.00		

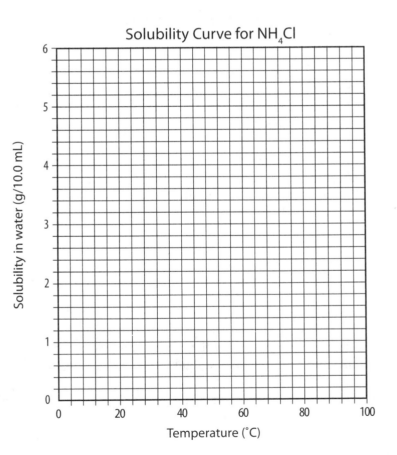

Solubility Curve for NH$_4$Cl

13 CHEMICAL THERMODYNAMICS

13A HOT SHOT
Finding the Specific Heat of a Metal

For about three years, the Spanish and French had been hammering the British fortress at Gibraltar. It had been the longest siege that the British had ever endured. Their forces were spread thin, since the War for American Independence was raging on the other side of the Atlantic Ocean. Spanish and French forces had been blockading Gibraltar, erecting floating forts stashed with 138 heavy guns to keep British supply ships from reaching the fortress. A fleet of ships supported the floating forts. British ships had managed to sneak past the blockade several times to bring much-needed provisions, but a grand assault was imminent.

The attack came on September 13, 1782. Thousands of Spanish and French troops pounded the British battery at Gibraltar from the floating forts. Thousands more people came to watch the spectacle from the neighboring hills just across the Spanish border. The British responded with red-hot shot, cannon balls heated to glowing before being fired at the wooden and very flammable floating forts and the support fleet. Hundreds of men were killed, and three out of the ten floating forts were destroyed, the rest scuttled by the Spanish because of damage. By springtime, the siege at Gibraltar was over. Heated metal shot had done the job!

Figure 1 This painting depicts the defeat of the floating forts at Gibraltar.

name _____

section _____ date _____

Objectives

✓ Observe thermal energy transfer in a calorimeter.

✓ Use equations to track the thermal energy involved in heat transfer.

✓ Calculate the specific heat of a metal from experimental data.

Equipment

laboratory scale (accurate to 0.01 g)

thermometer (accurate to 0.1 °C)

laboratory burner and lighter

wire gauze

ring stand and ring

rubber stopper, 1-hole, #4, split

beaker, 250 mL

beaker, 400 mL

graduated cylinder, 100 mL

test tube, large

test tube holder

foam cups, 6–8 oz (2)

cardboard, 4 × 4 in.

plastic wrap, approximately 1 × 1 in.

metal shot, 50–70 g

You've probably noticed how easily metal heats up. This is because of its specific heat. In very simple terms, specific heat is the measure of how easily something heats up. Something that is easy to heat up, like a metal, has a low specific heat. This means that it doesn't take a lot of thermal energy to raise its temperature by 1 °C. On the other hand, something with a high specific heat, like water, takes a lot of thermal energy to raise its temperature. You've heard the expression, "A watched pot never boils!"

Figure 2 Professional chemists use a Dewar flask (above) when they want to do accurate calorimetry experiments. The calorimeter that you will be using will allow just a little thermal energy to leak into the environment, though it is sufficient for this lab.

But what is the source of the thermal energy? It comes from another object. You've learned that thermal energy flows from hotter objects to cooler objects until they are the same temperature, that is, when they reach thermal equilibrium. You've also learned that the sum of all forms of energy is constant in any reaction or process; this is a statement of the *law of energy conservation*. The flow of thermal energy is heat. If this happens inside a special insulated container, known as a *calorimeter*, the amount of thermal energy lost by the hotter object will basically equal the amount of thermal energy gained by the cooler object.

In this lab, you will add some heated metal shot, your own miniature assault at Gibraltar, to much cooler water inside a calorimeter. You'll observe the thermal energy transfer to determine the specific heat of the metal.

PROCEDURE

Setting Up

❶ Assemble a ring stand and ring, and place the wire gauze on the ring (see Figure 3).

❷ Fill a 250 mL beaker three-quarters full with hot water and place it on the wire gauze, positioning your laboratory burner under the gauze. Light the laboratory burner and begin heating the water.

❸ While the water is heating, weigh the dry, large test tube and square of plastic wrap together on the balance to the nearest 0.01 g. Record this mass in Table 1.

❹ Add enough dry metal shot to fill half of the test tube. Cover the opening of the test tube with the plastic wrap, and then weigh the test tube to the nearest 0.01 g. Record this mass in Table 1.

❺ Now calculate the mass of metal shot that you are using. Record the result in Table 1.

Heating Up

❶ Place the covered test tube containing the metal shot into the beaker of water and bring the water to a boil. It is important to keep the plastic wrap over the end of the tube while it is heating in order to prevent water from getting inside the test tube.

1. How do you think you will determine the temperature of the metal shot?

_____

_____

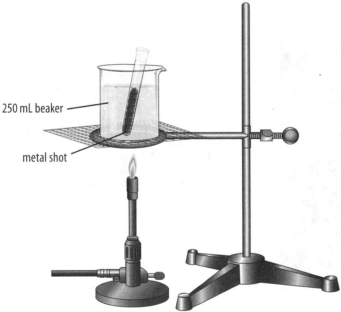

250 mL beaker

metal shot

Figure 3 Setup for heating metal shot in a hot water bath

❷ *Allow the water to boil for at least 10 minutes before obtaining its temperature.* Be sure the thermometer is not touching the sides or bottom of the beaker when you measure the temperature of the water to the nearest 0.1 °C. Record the result in Table 1. This is the initial temperature of the metal.

❸ While the metal sample is heating, weigh two nested foam cups to the nearest 0.01 g. Record this value in Table 1. This is your calorimeter.

❹ Using a 100 mL graduated cylinder, measure about 50 mL of distilled water into the inner cup and weigh the cups again to the nearest 0.01 g.

❺ Now calculate the mass of water that you are using in your calorimeter. Record the result in Table 1.

2. Is the metal shot going to be gaining or losing thermal energy in the calorimeter? Explain.

_____

_____

3. Is the water going to be gaining or losing thermal energy in the calorimeter? Explain.

_____

_____

4. Write a word equation that relates the heat of the water and the heat of the metal. Since one is losing heat, you will need to include a negative sign on that side of the equation.

_____

5. Substitute the formula for thermal energy into your equation, remembering to keep the water on one side and the metal on the other.

_____

6. Rearrange this equation to solve for the specific heat of the metal. This is what you are looking for! Show your work in the margin if needed.

_____

Using the Calorimeter

❶ Place the nested cups into the 400 mL beaker to give them more stability.

❷ Insert the thermometer into the split rubber stopper, using a drop or two of liquid soap to lubricate it. Adjust the position of the stopper on the thermometer so that the bulb of the thermometer does not touch the bottom of the inner cup when it is inserted through the hole in the cardboard lid (see Figure 4).

❸ Measure the initial temperature of the water in the foam cup calorimeter to the nearest 0.1 °C. Record this value in Table 1.

name _____

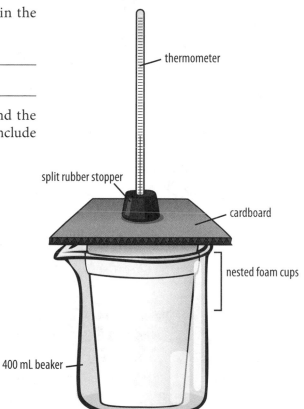

thermometer

split rubber stopper

cardboard

nested foam cups

400 mL beaker

Figure 4 Setting up the foam cup calorimeter

⚠ **Rubber Stoppers and Broken Thermometers**

Be sure that you wear gloves and exercise caution when inserting the thermometer into the split rubber stopper. Use soap as a lubricant, and don't put a force on the thermometer that could cause it to break.

7. What is the difference between the symbols *t* and *T*?

_____

_____

8. Why are you using *t* and not *T* in this lab?

_____

_____

_____

❹ Using the test tube holder, remove the test tube from the boiling water, take off the plastic wrap, and quickly pour the metal shot into the calorimeter. ***Be careful not to get any drops of hot water into the calorimeter or to splash water from the calorimeter when you pour in the metal shot!*** Cover the top with the cardboard lid and swirl the mixture carefully.

❺ Note the temperature of the water about every 30 seconds and record the highest temperature reached to the nearest 0.1 °C in Table 1. This is the final temperature of both the metal and the water.

9. At this point, what has happened to the flow of thermal energy?

_____

_____

❻ Calculate the change in temperature of the metal and the water. Record these results in Table 1.

10. Consider the changes in temperature. Did the water and metal do what you anticipated in Questions 2 and 3?

_____

_____

❼ Carefully decant into the sink as much water as possible without losing any metal shot. Pour the wet metal shot into the designated container so that it can dry.

11. Use the rearranged equation from Question 6 to solve for the specific heat of the metal, using the data you need from Table 1. Show your work in the margin if needed and report proper significant digits.

_____

12. Using the actual value for the specific heat of the metal supplied by your teacher, calculate the percent error for your experimental value. Show your work in the margin if needed.

name _____

_____

13. List at least three possible sources of error in your experiment.

_____

_____

_____

_____

Questions 14–16 are examples of experimental error. For each statement, determine whether these errors would make the experimental specific heat of the metal larger, smaller, or unchanged, and explain why.

14. Some hot metal spilled onto the table during its transfer into the calorimeter.

_____

15. The thermometer readings were all in error by being 2.3 °C higher than the actual temperature.

_____

16. The recorded mass of the water in the cup was too large.

_____

Maybe you are not accustomed to thinking about heat as something that can be productive. Heat transfer can be very useful because it can be used to generate electricity. This usually happens when heat is used to generate steam, which can turn a turbine.

17. Suggest some ways that heat transfer can be used to generate steam for electricity generation.

_____

_____

_____

Heat can also be a waste product. When factories put out heated air or heated water, it can cause problems in the environment.

18. Suggest some problems that waste heat can cause in the environment.

_____

_____

_____

19. Suggest a way to deal with waste heat.

_____

_____

_____

Table 1	
Mass of test tube and plastic wrap	
Mass of test tube, plastic wrap, and metal	
Mass of metal	
Temperature of boiling water (t_i for metal)	
Mass of cups	
Mass of cups and water	
Mass of water	
Temperature of water in cups (t_i for water)	
Temperature of water and metal (t_f for both)	
Change in water temperature (Δt)	
Change in metal temperature (Δt)	

13B SNOW MONKEYS
Exploring Enthalpies of Solution and Reaction

name _____

section _____   date _____

In the northern mountains of Japan, deep snow covers the rocky hillsides and trees. Subzero temperatures are the norm here. This is not the type of place you expect to see monkeys!

But monkeys do live here. Hot springs warmed by tectonic activity brings unexpected warmth to this cold, seemingly inhospitable place. And the monkeys love it. The Japanese macaque spends much of the winter foraging for food and lazing in the luxuriant heat of the springs. Their red faces make them look like they've been there a little too long! Hot springs warming monkeys is one of the happy effects of thermal energy transfer.

How does thermal energy transfer relate to enthalpy? When you think of enthalpy, you probably think of those two pages in your textbook that provide values for different reactions. And how did scientists find out the enthalpy for all those reactions? It is the same process of calorimetry that you followed in Lab 13A.

You'll be finding the enthalpy of two different processes: the enthalpy of solution of potassium nitrate (KNO_3) and the enthalpy of reaction of hydrochloric acid (HCl) with magnesium. The thermal energy changes that you measure in your calorimeter are the enthalpy when the pressure is held constant.

$$Q = \Delta H$$

You'll need to do some calculations to make sure that your units are correct, since enthalpy is measured in kJ/mol.

Snow monkeys enjoy thermal energy transfer; let's go do some thermal energy transfer of our own!

Objectives

✓ Determine the enthalpy change for a solution process.
✓ Determine the enthalpy changes for two chemical reactions.

Equipment

laboratory scale (accurate to 0.01 g)
ring stand and ring
thermometer, accurate to 0.1 °C
graduated cylinder, 100 mL
beaker, 600 mL
sandpaper
foam cups, 6–8 oz (2)
test tube clamp
rubber stopper, 1-hole, #4, split
cardboard, 4 × 4 in.
weighing paper
potassium nitrate (KNO_3), solid
hydrochloric acid (HCl), 1.00 *M*
magnesium ribbon, 0.10–0.15 g

Figure 1 Japanese macaques are the most northern-dwelling monkeys on Earth. They live in a protected area of Japan near the site of the 1998 Winter Olympics.

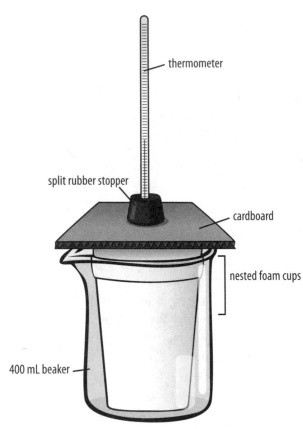

thermometer

split rubber stopper

cardboard

nested foam cups

400 mL beaker

Figure 2 Setting up the foam cup calorimeter

⚠️ **Rubber Stoppers and Broken Thermometers**

Be sure that you wear gloves and exercise caution when inserting the thermometer into the split rubber stopper. Use soap as a lubricant, and don't put a force on the thermometer that could cause it to break.

Weighing Weighing Paper?

If you have an electronic balance, tare or zero the balance with the weighing paper on it before adding KNO_3 so that you don't need to weigh the weighing paper and reweigh it with the KNO_3 on it.

PROCEDURE

Setting Up

❶ Nest the two foam cups together and place them inside a 600 mL glass beaker for added stability as shown in Figure 2.

❷ Insert the thermometer into the split rubber stopper, using a drop or two of liquid soap to lubricate it. Adjust the position of the stopper on the thermometer so that the bulb of the thermometer does not touch the bottom of the inner cup when it is inserted through the hole in the cardboard lid.

Heat of Solution

❶ Measure 50.0 mL of water with a large graduated cylinder. Pour this water into the inner foam cup.

1. What is your starting mass? How do you know?

_____

_____

❷ Determine the temperature of this water to the nearest 0.1 °C. Be sure that the thermometer bulb is completely submerged in the water. Record this value in Table 1.

❸ Determine the mass of a piece of weighing paper to the nearest 0.01 g. Record this value in Table 1.

❹ While the weighing paper is still on the balance, add 3–4 g of KNO_3. Measure this combined mass and record it in Table 1.

❺ Calculate the mass of KNO_3. Record this value in Table 1.

2. Write a balanced chemical equation that shows the solution process of KNO_3. Don't include the water in the equation since it just makes the salt dissociate.

_____

❻ Add the KNO_3 to the water, covering your calorimeter with the cardboard lid. Swirl the calorimeter gently while closely observing the temperature.

❼ Watch the temperature over a period of several minutes and record the most extreme (final) temperature to the nearest 0.1 °C in Table 1.

3. In this process, were you expecting the water to release or absorb heat?

_____

Since ΔH_{soln} is expressed as J/mol (or kJ/mol), you must calculate the thermal energy and the moles of KNO_3, and then divide those answers to get J/mol.

4. Calculate the thermal energy change of the water. Show your work in the margin if needed.

name _____

_____

The temperature of the solution changed because the potassium nitrate broke up into ions. The change in temperature of the water also gives us the change in temperature of the KNO_3.

5. Now calculate the moles of KNO_3 that dissolved in the water. Show your work in the margin if needed.

_____

6. Express the enthalpy in kJ/mol. Show your work in the margin if needed.

_____

7. Calculate a percent error based on the standard value for the enthalpy of solution of KNO_3. This value is $\Delta H°_{sol} = +34.89$ kJ/mol. Show your work in the margin if needed.

_____

8. Is your value for enthalpy positive or negative? How does this relate to your observations in Question 3?

_____

_____

Heat of Reaction

❶ Empty the calorimeter, rinse well with water, and allow to drain.

❷ Measure 75.0 mL of 1.00 *M* HCl solution in a graduated cylinder and pour it into the inner cup.

❸ Measure the temperature of the HCl in the cup to the nearest 0.1 °C. Record this value in Table 2.

❹ Clean the magnesium ribbon with sandpaper, and then wipe it with a clean paper towel.

❺ Measure the mass of the clean metal to the nearest 0.01 g. Record this value in Table 2.

❻ Roll the magnesium ribbon into a loose ball, drop it into the acid, and cover the cup.

This is an example of what happens when a metal reacts with a strong acid. This process usually liberates hydrogen gas and forms a salt with the anion of the acid and an ionized form of the metal, which will be a cation.

❼ While gently swirling the cup, observe the temperature constantly. The metal should dissolve completely. Record the most extreme (final) temperature reached to the nearest 0.1 °C in Table 2.

⚠ **Flammable Hydrogen!**

This reaction generates minimal hydrogen gas because you are using a fairly dilute hydrochloric acid. Nevertheless, make sure there are no ignited burners or flames nearby when doing this lab.

9. What did you observe during this reaction?

_____

_____

10. Write a balanced equation that shows the reaction of HCl with Mg to liberate hydrogen gas and form a salt.

_____

In contrast to Lab 13A, now you will calculate the theoretical enthalpy of the reaction. You've had lots of practice doing this in your textbook. Use the balanced reaction from Question 10 and the standard values provided in the margin.

11. Calculate the enthalpy of reaction between HCl and Mg. Show your work in the margin if needed.

_____

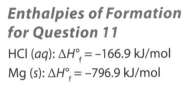

Enthalpies of Formation for Question 11

HCl (aq): $\Delta H°_f = -166.9$ kJ/mol

Mg (s): $\Delta H°_f = -796.9$ kJ/mol

12. Calculate the thermal energy change of the HCl that actually happened. Express your answer in kilojoules and be sure to use the proper sign!

_____

In this case, the magnesium was the limiting reactant for the reaction. Because of this, you will use the amount of Mg that reacted in your calculation of the enthalpy of reaction.

13. Calculate the moles of Mg that reacted. Do your math in the margin space.

_____

14. Express enthalpy in kJ/mol.

_____

15. Calculate a percent error using the enthalpies of reaction that you calculated in Questions 11 and 14.

_____

16. Is your value for enthalpy positive or negative? How does this relate to your observations from Questions 9 and 11?

_____

_____

Figure 3 Photo etching is used to produce circuit boards in laptops, computers, and smartphones. It uses the process of reacting a metal with an acid.

On a small scale, people use the reaction of a metal such as copper with sulfuric acid and iron (III) chloride in a process called *photo etching*. This basically allows people to "print" a circuit that can be used in a circuit board. (You'll learn more about semiconductors and integrated circuits in Chapter 19.) During this process, the acid is heated to speed up the reaction.

17. Why does heating the acid speed up the process?

_____

_____

18. Suggest another way to use the process of etching.

name _____

_____

_____

_____

Table 1 Enthalpy of Solution	
Initial temperature of water	
Mass of weighing paper	
Mass of weighing paper and KNO_3	
Mass of KNO_3	
Final temperature of the KNO_3 and water solution	

Table 2 Enthalpy of Reaction	
Initial temperature of HCl solution	
Mass of magnesium ribbon	
Final temperature of HCl and magnesium ribbon reaction	

14 CHEMICAL KINETICS

14 COLLISION COURSE
Concentration and Reaction Rates

name _____

section _____ date _____

It was a first in history—a comet was breaking apart, and its fragments were on a collision course with Jupiter. Of course, the fact that two astronomical bodies were going to collide wasn't unusual. This moment was historic because people were watching it happen live for the first time!

Figure 1 The collision between comet Shoemaker-Levy 9 and Jupiter in 1994 showed how Jupiter acts as a cosmic vacuum cleaner, attracting and consuming cosmic debris in its neighborhood. The circled area is where a fragment of the comet struck the planet.

Objectives

✓ Observe how concentration affects reaction rates.

✓ Explain this effect using the collision theory.

✓ Determine the concentration of an unknown substance on the basis of its reaction rate.

Equipment

stopwatch
laser pointer
ring stand
buret clamp
burets, 50 mL (2)
beakers, 150 mL (2)
graduated cylinder, 10 mL
test tube rack
test tubes (12)
masking tape or grease pencil
hydrochloric acid (HCl), 1.0 M
sodium thiosulfate ($Na_2S_2O_3$), 0.10 M

In July of 1994, scientists at NASA captured the first-ever footage of a collision between two solar system objects. The collision lacerated parts of Jupiter's paisley-like surface. Through this collision, scientists learned more about what was beneath the surface of Jupiter.

Chemistry is a collision course—that is, a course about collisions! For two substances to react, the particles that comprise them must collide with enough force and in the proper orientation (see Figure 2). And the more collisions that particles experience, the faster they will react.

The *rate* of a chemical reaction is the speed at which the reaction proceeds. It can also be defined either as the amount of product formed per unit of time or the amount of reactant consumed per unit of time. To change how fast a reaction takes place, you need to change the number of collisions that happen within a certain length of time.

In this experiment, you will explore how varying the concentration of a reactant affects how fast a reaction takes place. Three, two, one … *blast off!*

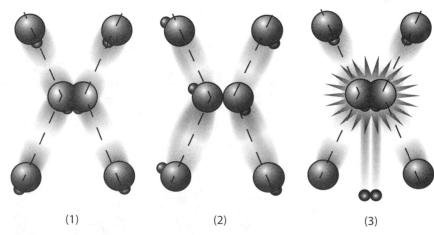

(1)   (2)   (3)

Figure 2 Collisions have three possible results: (1) proper orientation but not enough force, (2) enough force but improper orientation, or (3) proper orientation and enough force. Only the third result produces a reaction.

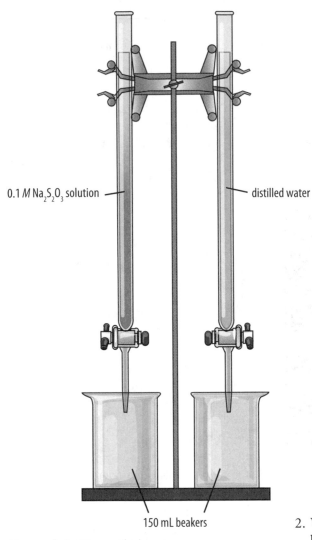

0.1 M Na$_2$S$_2$O$_3$ solution — distilled water

150 mL beakers

Figure 3 Setting up the burets

The Tyndall Effect

In Chapter 12, you learned about the Tyndall effect. Check page 328 of your textbook to refresh your memory about how light relates to solutions.

Table 1		
Test tube	Volume of 0.10 M Na$_2$S$_2$O$_3$	Volume of water
1	5.0 mL	0.0 mL
2	4.0 mL	1.0 mL
3	3.0 mL	2.0 mL
4	2.0 mL	3.0 mL
5	1.0 mL	4.0 mL

PROCEDURE

Setting Up

❶ Set up two burets and one buret clamp on a ring stand as shown in Figure 3.

❷ Fill one buret with 0.10 M Na$_2$S$_2$O$_3$ and the other with distilled water.

❸ Put a 150 mL beaker under each buret, and drain a little liquid from each buret to fill their tips. Stop when the water level reaches the 0 mL mark.

❹ Place 12 clean test tubes in a test tube rack. Be sure that they have no water in them. Label five of them as Tubes 1, 2, … 5 using masking tape or a grease pencil. Label one "unknown."

❺ Use a graduated cylinder to add 5.0 mL of 1.0 M HCl to each of the six *unlabeled* test tubes. Measure accurately!

❻ Prepare mixtures of 0.10 M Na$_2$S$_2$O$_3$ and water in Tubes 1–5 according to the proportions given in Table 1 in the margin at the bottom of this page. The test tube labeled "unknown" should remain empty.

1. You will be making mixtures of the Na$_2$S$_2$O$_3$ solutions and water according to Table 1. Why is it important that the test tubes have no water in them?

_____

_____

_____

2. While your test tubes are in the rack, shine the laser pointer through both the Na$_2$S$_2$O$_3$ and HCl solutions. What do you observe? What do you conclude from your observation?

_____

_____

_____

The reaction that you will use is the decomposition of the thiosulfate ion, S$_2$O$_3^{2-}$, supplied by the compound sodium thiosulfate, Na$_2$S$_2$O$_3$, by reacting it with an acid, HCl. The Na$^+$ and Cl$^-$ ions are both spectator ions in this reaction. The thiosulfate ion decomposes in the presence of acid to form elemental sulfur and sulfurous acid.

3. Write a balanced equation that shows this reaction.

_____

4. Elemental sulfur is a nonreactive, nonpolar substance. Do you think it will dissolve in water? Explain.

_____

_____

5. How do you think you will know when the reaction begins?

name _____

_____

_____

6. How will you measure the rate of reaction?

_____

_____

_____

Measuring Reaction Rates

❶ As quickly as possible, mix one tube of HCl with each of the five tubes of sodium thiosulfate. Start the stopwatch.

❷ Every 10 seconds, shine the laser pointer through the tubes. When the reaction starts producing sulfur, the laser beam will become visible in the tube as a red line. When this happens, note the tube number and the time to the nearest 10 s. If you want, you may take the tubes from the rack one at a time and check them individually with the pointer. Record your results in Table 2 on page 143.

❸ Pour a 5.0 mL sample of a solution of $Na_2S_2O_3$ of unknown molarity into the clean, dry test tube labeled "unknown."

❹ Mix the unknown with the last test tube containing 1.0 M HCl. Measure the time that it takes for this solution to become cloudy when mixed with 5.0 mL of 1.0 M HCl. Record this value in Table 2 to the nearest 10s.

❺ Calculate the moles of thiosulfate ion, $S_2O_3^{2-}$, for Tubes 2–5. Record your results in Table 3. Show your work in the margin if needed. (The values for the first tube have been calculated for you.)

❻ Calculate the concentration of $S_2O_3^{2-}$ in moles per liter (M) using the total volume in each test tube, including the volume of 1.0 M HCl. Show your work in the margin if needed. Record your results in Table 2.

❼ Now, plot the data from Table 2 in the graphing area at the end of the lab, with the concentration of thiosulfate on the x-axis and the reaction time on the y-axis. Draw a smooth curve through the points.

7. What happens to the time required for the reaction and the rate of the reaction as the concentration of the thiosulfate ion increases?

_____

_____

_____

8. Using your graph, estimate the concentration of thiosulfate in your unknown solution.

_____

_____

_____

9. Check the six test tubes. Has any sulfur settled out? What does the answer to that question indicate?

_____

_____

10. Is it accurate to assume that doubling the concentration will halve the reaction rate? Explain.

_____

_____

11. How do you think scientists and manufacturers could use this relationship?

_____

_____

_____

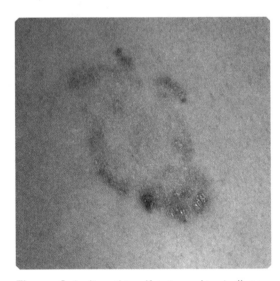

Figure 4 Sodium thiosulfate is used topically to treat ringworm, a type of fungal infection.

In 2009, there was a fire at a nightclub in Perm, Russia. Over 100 people died as the burning insulation released cyanide. Many of the deaths and hospitalizations related to this accident were a result of cyanide poisoning.

Sodium thiosulfate can be administered intravenously to patients who experience both arsenic and cyanide poisoning. Increasing the concentration allows their bodies to eliminate the cyanide as the sodium thiosulfate binds to the cyanide to help it pass harmlessly through the body.

12. How does this example of chemical kinetics work to alleviate people's suffering?

_____

_____

_____

name _____

Table 2

Test tube	Reaction time (s)	Concentration of $S_2O_3^{2-}$ (M)
1		
2		
3		
4		
5		
unknown		—

Table 3

Test tube	Volume of $Na_2S_2O_3$	Volume of water	Volume of 1.0 M HCl	Total volume	Moles of $S_2O_3^{2-}$	Molarity of $S_2O_3^{2-}$
1	5.0 mL	0.0 mL	5.0 mL	10.0 mL	0.00050 mol	0.050 M
2						
3						.
4						
5						

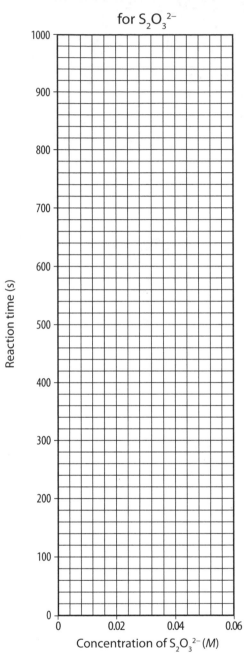

15 CHEMICAL EQUILIBRIUM

15 OLD FAITHFUL
Explorations in Equilibrium

name _____

section _____ date _____

It happens like clockwork almost every 91 minutes. Water spews 125 feet into the air, accompanied by billows of steam. Old Faithful geyser in Yellowstone National Park erupts as superheated water under pressure works its way through cracks in the ground. The formation of steam from liquid water and back to water from steam as it condenses on the ground around the geyser are an example of a reversible process.

Similarly, many reactions are *reversible*. That means that both reactants can form products in the *forward reaction*, and the products can form reactants in the *reverse reaction*. And this can happen at the same time! At first, the forward reaction proceeds quickly and then slows down as the reactants are used up. On the other hand, the reverse reaction is very slow at first, but it speeds up as more products are formed. Eventually the rate of the forward reaction equals the rate of the reverse reaction. We then have *equilibrium*! See Figure 2. Since both reactions are now proceeding at the same rate, the concentration of each type of ion or molecule remains constant. These reactions are predictable, just like the eruptions of Old Faithful.

Objectives
- ✓ Observe equilibrium in a chemical reaction.
- ✓ Vary concentration in this chemical reaction to observe changes in equilibrium according to Le Châtelier's principle.
- ✓ Vary temperature in this chemical reaction to observe changes in equilibrium.

Equipment
laboratory burner and lighter
Erlenmeyer flask, 250 mL
rubber stopper
test tube holder
test tube rack
test tubes (7)
transfer pipets (2)
iron (III) chloride ($FeCl_3$), 0.25 *M*
potassium chloride (KCl), solid
potassium thiocyanate (KSCN), 0.25 *M*
masking tape or grease pencil

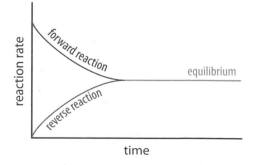

Figure 1 What two reversible processes are at work in this photo?

In this experiment, you will be exploring how the equilibrium establishes and changes in the reaction of solutions of iron (III) chloride and potassium thiocyanate. How will you know what is happening? You'll observe equilibrium changes by observing changes in the color of the solution. It's time to explore the exact nature of equilibrium.

Figure 2 Equilibrium in a reversible reaction

Throughout this experiment, make sure that you do not contaminate the two solutions with each other.

PROCEDURE

Setting Up

❶ Label one test tube "FeCl$_3$" and another "KSCN."

❷ Pour approximately 3 mL of iron (III) chloride solution and 3 mL of potassium thiocyanate solution in the appropriately labeled test tubes. Put a pipet in each of the two test tubes.

1. What color is the iron (III) chloride solution?

_____

2. What color is the potassium thiocyanate solution?

_____

❸ Using separate pipets for each solution, add 20 drops each of the iron (III) chloride solution and potassium thiocyanate solutions to 100 mL of water in the 250 mL Erlenmeyer flask. Mix thoroughly by swirling the contents.

3. Write the balanced reaction of iron (III) chloride and potassium thiocyanate to form iron (III) thiocyanate and potassium chloride.

_____

4. Potassium chloride forms a colorless solution. On the basis of your observation of this reaction, what color do you think the iron (III) thiocyanate forms in solution?

_____

❹ Label an additional five test tubes as Tubes 1, 2,…, 5. Fill each one half full with the solution from the flask. Set aside Tube 1 for color comparison. Record your observations for Tube 1 in Table 1.

Shifting Equilibrium

According to Le Châtelier's principle, the reaction equilibrium that you just started will shift to offset changes in concentration or temperature.

5. Consider the equation that you wrote in Question 3. Which direction would the equilibrium shift if you were to add more KSCN? What color change would you observe?

_____

_____

6. If you added more FeCl$_3$, which direction would the equilibrium shift? What color change would you observe?

_____

_____

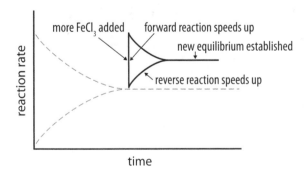

Figure 3 Original (- - -) and new (—) equilibrium. Notice that the rates of both reactions are greater than they were in the original equilibrium.

7. If you added more KCl, which direction would the equilibrium shift? What color change would you observe?

name _____

_____

_____

Now let's see how good your predictions are!

❶ To Tube 2, add 20 drops of the KSCN solution. Record the color change in Table 1 by comparing the tube to the solution in Tube 1, the color-reference tube.

8. How does this compare to your prediction in Question 5? Explain your observation by describing what is happening to the forward and reverse rates of reaction.

_____

_____

_____

_____

9. What happened to the concentrations of $Fe(SCN)_3$, KCl, and $FeCl_3$?

_____

_____

❷ To Tube 3, add 20 drops of $FeCl_3$ solution. Record the color change in Table 1 by comparing the tube to the solution in the color-reference tube.

10. How does this compare to your prediction in Question 6? Explain your observation by describing what is happening to the forward and reverse rates of reaction.

_____

_____

_____

_____

11. What happened to the concentrations of $Fe(SCN)_3$, KCl, and KSCN?

_____

_____

❸ To Tube 4, add approximately 1 g of solid KCl, close with a rubber stopper, and shake it well. Record the color change in Table 1 by comparing the tube to the solution in the color-reference tube.

12. How does this compare to your prediction in Question 7? Explain your observation by describing what is happening to the forward and reverse rates of reaction.

_____

_____

_____

_____

13. What happened to the concentrations of $Fe(SCN)_3$, $FeCl_3$, and KSCN?

_____

_____

What Goes Where?

By step ❹, the contents of your test tubes should be as follows:

- **Tube 1:** mixture only (reference tube)
- **Tube 2:** mixture + 20 drops KSCN
- **Tube 3:** mixture + 20 drops $FeCl_3$
- **Tube 4:** mixture + 1 g KCl
- **Tube 5:** mixture + heat

❹ Light the laboratory burner and adjust for a low flame. Using the test tube holder, move Tube 5 back and forth over the flame until you notice a change in color. Record the color change in Table 1 by comparing the tube to the solution in the color-reference tube.

14. In which direction did the equilibrium shift when Tube 5 was heated? How can you tell?

_____

_____

15. What happened to the concentrations of KCl, $Fe(SCN)_3$, $FeCl_3$, and KSCN?

_____

_____

16. On the basis of the way the equilibrium shifted, would you say the chemical equation is exothermic or endothermic as written? Explain your answer.

_____

_____

_____

17. Suggest another way to test if the reaction is exothermic or endothermic as written.

name _____

_____

_____

_____

_____

18. Oil refineries and many types of chemical plants use refrigerators during the manufacturing process. Why do you think they do this?

_____

_____

Figure 4 From a chemical reaction standpoint, why do you use a refrigerator?

_____

_____

Table 1	
Color of FeCl$_3$ and KSCN when mixed in Tube 1	
Color when KSCN was added to the mixture in Tube 2	
Color when FeCl$_3$ was added to the mixture in Tube 3	
Color when KCl was added to the mixture in Tube 4	
Color when mixture was heated in Tube 5	

16 ACIDS, BASES, AND SALTS

16A RAINBOW OF CHEMISTRY
Acid-Base Indicators

name _____

section _____   date _____

Perhaps you think of acid-base indicators as something that is found only in the chemistry laboratory. But they're actually everywhere! Many are chemicals that come from the natural world. The leaves of red cabbage, the flowers of geraniums and poppies, the stems of rhubarb, and the fruit of blueberries, cherries, and black currants contain chemicals that are natural acid-base indicators. Litmus, the indicator with which you're probably most familiar, comes from a lichen! With the right combination of indicators, you can cover the whole pH spectrum. Of course, pH meters give you a more accurate and objective reading on pH, but indicators are useful because they are more widely available.

But how do acid-base indicators work? They generally are weak organic acids or bases that exist in equilibrium between the conjugate acid-base pair. The conjugate acid of an indicator has a different color than the conjugate base. The equation below shows this.

$$HIn\ (aq) + H_2O\ (l) \rightleftharpoons H_3O^+\ (aq) + In^-\ (aq)$$

color 1   color 2

According to Le Châtelier's principle, changes in the concentration of H_3O^+ will shift the equilibrium, affecting the color of the indicator. When the color changes, we can know what's happening to the hydronium concentration just by looking at the solution.

Of course, if there is more than one indicator present in a solution, a greater range of colors is possible. How acidic or basic the solution must be to favor one color over the other depends on the specific indicator; each indicator has its own pH range over which its color will change. Using several indicators allows you to match a solution of unknown concentration to a standard. Although the color of your solution may not match a standard exactly, your estimated $[H_3O^+]$ will be fairly close.

In this experiment, you'll try your hand at making a rainbow of chemistry. You will make three sets of standards. Each set will cover a range of five concentrations and will contain an acid-base indicator. You'll use these colors to estimate the concentration of the hydronium ion and the pH of these solutions. Follow that rainbow!

Objectives

✓ Prepare a set of indicator standards.
✓ Explain how acid-base indicators work.
✓ Estimate the $[H_3O^+]$ of an acetic acid ($HC_2H_3O_2$) solution.
✓ Find the acid-ionization constant (K_a) of an unknown weak acid.
✓ Relate acid strength with the value of the acid-ionization constant.

Equipment

graduated cylinder, 10 mL
graduated cylinder, 100 mL
test tube racks (2)
test tubes (21)
transfer pipet (eyedropper)
masking tape or grease pencil
thymol blue solution
methyl orange solution
methyl red solution
hydrochloric acid (HCl), 0.1 *M*
acetic acid ($HC_2H_3O_2$), 0.1 *M*
unknown weak acid, 1.0 *M*
pH probe (optional)

Figure 1 Hydrangea petals carry a chemical that turns blue in acidic soil (left) and pink in alkaline soil (right).

Water to Acid?

Normally, it isn't good lab procedure to add water to acid because the acid can spatter and injure the user. However, in this setting, you are using extremely dilute acids. Diluting this way is easier than measuring out the water and then adding the acid.

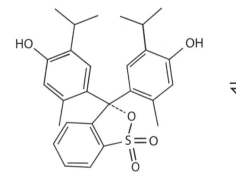

Table 1			
HCl	Thymol blue	Methyl orange	Methyl red
0.1 *M*	1A	2A	3A
0.01 *M*	1B	2B	3B
0.001 *M*	1C	2C	3C
0.0001 *M*	1D	2D	3D
0.0001 *M*	1E	2E	3E

Showing True Colors

You may want to put a piece of white paper behind your test tubes or hold them up to a light as you observe their colors.

PROCEDURE

Setting Up Indicators

❶ Label five test tubes "1A"–"1E," five test tubes "2A"–"2E," and five test tubes "3A"–"3E." Place them in the test tube racks.

❷ Measure 15 mL to the nearest 0.1 mL of 0.1 *M* (1×10^{-1} *M*) HCl solution in the 100 mL graduated cylinder.

❸ Using the 10 mL graduated cylinder, pour 3 mL portions of the HCl into Tubes 1A, 2A, and 3A. You should have 6 mL of 0.1 *M* HCl remaining in the 100 mL graduated cylinder.

❹ Add water up to the 60 mL mark and mix well. This dilutes the acid to 0.01 *M* (1×10^{-2} *M*) HCl.

❺ Rinse out the 10 mL graduated cylinder thoroughly and pour 3 mL portions of the 0.01 *M* HCl into Tubes 1B, 2B, and 3B.

❻ Repeat steps ❹ and ❺ to make the dilutions listed below and pour 3 mL into the test tubes specified. See Table 1 in the margin for the complete arrangement of test tubes and acid concentrations.

0.001 *M* (1×10^{-3} *M*) HCl in Tubes 1C, 2C, and 3C

0.0001 *M* (1×10^{-4} *M*) HCl in Tubes 1D, 2D, and 3D

0.00001 *M* (1×10^{-5} *M*) HCl in Tubes 1E, 2E, and 3E

❼ To each solution in Tubes 1A–E, add three drops of thymol blue solution. Swirl the solutions well and record the color of each in Table 2 on page 156.

1. In Figure 2, how does the structure of thymol blue change, indicated by a color change?

_____

_____

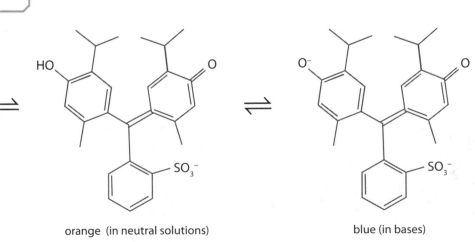

red (in acids)   orange (in neutral solutions)   blue (in bases)

Figure 2 Thymol blue is an artificial indicator that can undergo two color changes. From left to right, these structures produce red in acids, orange in neutral solutions, and blue in basic solutions. Study these three structures to see how the structure changes with each color change.

2. Which structure do you have in your test tubes right now?

_____

_____

❽ For Tubes 2A–E, add three drops of methyl orange solution. For Tubes 3A–E, add three drops of methyl red solution. Swirl the solutions well and record the color of each in Table 2.

❾ (Optional) Use a pH probe to measure the exact pH of your dilutions in all 15 tubes to the nearest 0.1. Make sure that you rinse the probe between tests. If a pH probe is not available, calculate the pH from $[H_3O^+]$ using the pH formula found on page 414 of your textbook. Record these values in Table 2.

3. What effect does a dilution by a factor of 10 (for example, from 1×10^{-7} to 1×10^{-8}) have on the pH of an HCl solution?

_____

4. On the basis of your answer to Question 3, describe how easy it is to change the pH of a solution.

_____

_____

_____

5. Estimate the pH range over which each of the indicators changes color.

_____

_____

Now you are going to use the indicator standards that you just created to learn more about the pH range in which they work best.

Comparing $HC_2H_3O_2$ to Standards

❶ Label three test tubes "4," "5," and "6." Measure 3.0 mL to the nearest 0.1 mL of 0.1 M $HC_2H_3O_2$ solution into these test tubes using the 10 mL graduated cylinder.

❷ Add three drops of thymol blue solution to Tube 4, three drops of methyl orange solution to Tube 5, and three drops of methyl red solution to Tube 6.

❸ Compare the color of Tube 4 to Tubes 1A–E from your indicator standards. Record your observations of color in Table 2.

❹ Compare the color of Tube 5 to Tubes 2A–E from your indicator standards. Record your observations of color in Table 2.

❺ Compare the color of Tube 6 to Tubes 3A–E from your indicator standards. Record your observations of color in Table 2.

❻ Use your observations from steps ❸ through ❺ to estimate the $[H_3O^+]$ in the $HC_2H_3O_2$ solution, and record your estimate in Table 2.

> ### More Tubes!
> **Tube 4**: 3.0 mL of 0.1 M $HC_2H_3O_2$
>   3 drops of thymol blue
> **Tube 5**: 3.0 mL of 0.1 M $HC_2H_3O_2$
>   3 drops of methyl orange
> **Tube 6**: 3.0 mL of 0.1 M $HC_2H_3O_2$
>   3 drops of methyl red

6. How do the strengths of HCl and the $HC_2H_3O_2$ compare? Explain how this affects their behavior.

_____

_____

_____

_____

❼ Using the estimated $[H_3O^+]$, record the pH of the 0.1 M $HC_2H_3O_2$ solution in Table 2.

7. How did you arrive at this estimate?

_____

_____

8. Compare the pH of $HC_2H_3O_2$ to the pH of the 1.0×10^{-3} M HCl. How do their concentrations and pHs compare? What does this mean?

_____

_____

_____

_____

_____

_____

Comparing an Unknown Acid to Standards

❶ Label three more test tubes "7," "8," and "9." Measure 3.0 mL to the nearest 0.1 mL of 0.1 M of the unknown weak acid solution into these test tubes using the 10 mL graduated cylinder.

❷ Add three drops of thymol blue solution to Tube 7, three drops of methyl orange solution to Tube 8, and three drops of methyl red solution to Tube 9.

❸ Compare the color of Tube 7 to Tubes 1A–E from your indicator standards and record your observations of color in Table 2.

❹ Compare the color of Tube 8 to Tubes 2A–E from your indicator standards. Record your observations of color in Table 2.

❺ Compare the color of Tube 9 to Tubes 3A–E from your indicator standards. Record your observations of color in Table 2.

❻ Use your observations from steps ❸ through ❺ to estimate the $[H_3O^+]$ of a 1.0 M unknown weak acid by comparing it to the indicator standards. Record your estimate in Table 2.

> **Even More Tubes!**
>
> **Tube 7**: 3.0 mL of 1.0 M unknown acid
>   3 drops of thymol blue
> **Tube 8**: 3.0 mL of 1.0 M unknown acid
>   3 drops of methyl orange
> **Tube 9**: 3.0 mL of 1.0 M unknown acid
>   3 drops of methyl red

Since we don't know the identity of this acid, let's give it the symbol HA to write some chemical reactions and equilibrium expressions.

9. Write an equilibrium chemical reaction for the dissociation of HA in water to form hydronium ions and a conjugate base.

_____

10. Using this reaction, write the K_a expression for this acid.

_____

You can make two simplifying assumptions here. First, since most of the molecules are un-ionized, you can assume that [HA] is approximately equal to the molarity (M) of the weak acid. Second, since each HA molecule ionizes to form one H_3O^+ and one A^-, you can assume that the value of the hydronium ion concentration, $[H_3O^+]$, equals the value of the anion concentration, $[A^-]$. Therefore, if you know the value for the hydronium ion concentration, you also know the value for the anion concentration.

11. What is $[A^-]$?

_____

12. What is [HA]?

_____

13. Use the K_a expression that you recorded in Question 10. Substitute values from your answers in Questions 11 and 12 and the value of $[H_3O^+]$ that you estimated in step ❻ and recorded in Table 2. Calculate the value of K_a. Show your work in the margin if needed.

_____

14. Ask your teacher for the identity of the acid. Use Table 16-4 from page 419 of your textbook to find its K_a value. Calculate a percent error.

_____

15. How do you think knowing the strength of an acid would make a difference?

_____

_____

_____

			Indicator Colors		
Test tubes	$[H_3O^+]$	pH	Thymol blue	Methyl orange	Methyl red
Group A	1.0×10^{-1}				
Group B	1.0×10^{-2}				
Group C	1.0×10^{-3}				
Group D	1.0×10^{-4}				
Group E	1.0×10^{-5}				
$HC_2H_3O_2$ (Tubes 4, 5, and 6)					
Unknown weak acid (Tubes 7, 8, and 9)		NA			

Table 2

16B CHEESY CHEMISTRY
Acid-Base Titration

name _____

section _____   date _____

It's 5:00 a.m. at Shelburne Farms—milking time. Brown Swiss cows leave behind the verdant Vermont fields dotted with dandelions to canter single-file into the milking pens. Here, 700 gallons of raw milk flow into the cheese-making vats to soon become blocks of cheddar cheese set to age in a cooler. But how do the cheese-makers at Shelburne Farms know when the cheese is ready?

This is where chemistry comes in. Farmers do a titration of the whey from cheese to determine its acidity. The acid in cheese is lactic acid, which is what helps cheese to develop taste and texture.

Figure 1 The process of cheese-making involves a surprising amount of chemistry, involving thermodynamics, equilibrium, chemical kinetics, organic chemistry, and acid-base chemistry.

Titration is a type of *volumetric analysis* in which you can find the concentration of an unknown solution by measuring the volume of a second known solution that reacts completely with the first. A volumetric analysis depends on measuring a volume accurately. Certain types of glassware—burets, pipets, and volumetric flasks—allow you to meet that requirement.

So how do we know when the unknown substance has completely reacted with the known substance? You've been learning about neutralization reactants. They produce a salt. But if the salt dissolves in water, we won't be able to see it. So for acid-base titrations, we usually use an indicator.

In this experiment, you will find the concentration of a vinegar by doing an acid-base titration. There are actually two steps to this. First, you have to make sure that you know the concentration of the known solution. In this case, it will be a NaOH solution. We'll do that by titrating it with a primary standard using phenolphthalein as the indicator. A *primary standard* is a chemical substance that is easy to work with and of such purity that it can be used as a reference. Your primary standard is an organic acid salt called *potassium hydrogen phthalate* ($KHC_8H_4O_4$), or *KHP* for short. Second, you'll use your standardized solution of NaOH and the indicator phenolphthalein to determine the molarity of acid in a sample of white vinegar.

Objectives

✓ Standardize a solution of sodium hydroxide, using potassium hydrogen phthalate as the primary standard.

✓ Perform the technique of titration.

✓ Calculate the molarity of white vinegar, using the standardized sodium hydroxide solution.

✓ Calculate the percent by mass of acetic acid contained in vinegar.

Equipment

laboratory scale (accurate to 0.01 g)
beakers, 150 mL (2)
buret clamp
burets, 100 mL (2)
ring stand
Erlenmeyer flask, 250 mL
eyedropper
filtering funnel
wash bottle
white vinegar
phenolphthalein solution
potassium hydrogen phthalate
   ($KHC_8H_4O_4$, or KHP)
sodium hydroxide (NaOH) solution

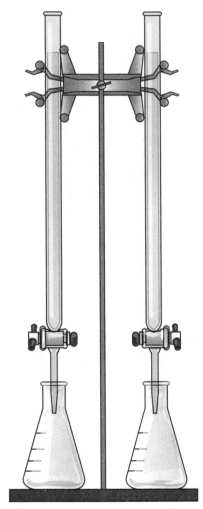

Figure 2 Acid-base titration setup

PROCEDURE

Setting Up

❶ Add about 100 mL of NaOH solution to a clean, dry 150 mL beaker.

❷ Set up the buret clamp on the ring stand as shown in Figure 2.

❸ Thoroughly clean one buret by rinsing it with water several times. Rinse the buret twice with a few milliliters of the NaOH solution. Be sure to rinse the tip as well, allowing solution to drain out of the buret. Then place the buret back in the clamp.

❹ Close the stopcock and, with the aid of a funnel, carefully fill the buret with NaOH solution. Open the stopcock and drain out some of the solution until the tip of the buret is filled. Add NaOH solution to the buret, if necessary, until the level of the liquid is near but not above 0 mL. Record the initial volume to the nearest 0.01 mL in the Trial 1 column of Table 1.

1. How is the calibration of a buret different from that of a graduated cylinder?

_____

_____

_____

_____

❺ Determine the mass of the 250 mL Erlenmeyer flask to the nearest 0.01 g. (It need not be dry inside.) Record this value in Table 1.

Standardizing the NaOH Solution

❶ Add 0.5–0.6 g of potassium hydrogen phthalate (KHP) to the flask on the scale. Record the combined weight to the nearest 0.01 g in Table 1.

❷ Use this information to calculate the mass of KHP ($KHC_8H_4O_4$) used. Record this result in Table 1.

2. Write a balanced chemical equation for the reaction of NaOH with KHP to form water and sodium potassium phthalate. (*Hint*: The phthalate ion is $C_8H_4O_4^{2-}$.)

_____

❸ Add about 30 mL of distilled water to the flask and swirl the flask until all the solid dissolves. Wash any crystals that cling to the wall of the flask down into the solution with a few milliliters of water from a wash bottle.

3. Why does the water not need to be measured accurately?

name _____

_____

_____

_____

_____

❹ Add two drops of phenolphthalein indicator to the KHP solution in the flask.

4. The structure of phenolphthalein is shown in Figure 3. Phenolphthalein is a white solid. But you are using drops of solution! Suggest what it might be dissolved in. (*Hint*: Think about the polarity of phenolphthalein.)

_____

_____

_____

_____

❺ Place the flask on a piece of white paper under the buret. You'll use this to help you see when the color in the flask starts to change. Lower the buret until the tip extends into the flask.

❻ Titrate the KHP solution by adding a few milliliters of NaOH solution from the buret as you swirl the flask to mix the solutions (see Figure 4). Stop adding NaOH when the light pink color doesn't go away with swirling. Read the final volume in the buret to the nearest 0.01 mL and record it in Table 1.

❼ Now you'll do Trial 2 for standardizing the solution. Refill the buret nearly to the 0 mL mark with NaOH solution and record that initial volume in the Trial 2 column of Table 1. Make a new sample of KHP solution as you did in steps ❶ through ❹, recording your data as you go. Make sure that you rinse out your flask well before making the new KHP solution.

❽ Do another titration of this new KHP solution as you did in step ❻. Record your final volume in Table 1.

❾ Calculate the amount of NaOH used in both trials and record this data in Table 1.

5. Describe the color change that you observed for phenolphthalein based on the acidity or basicity of the solution.

_____

_____

Using the grams of KHP that you measured into the solution and the volume of NaOH solution needed to react with all of it, you can calculate the molarity of the NaOH solution.

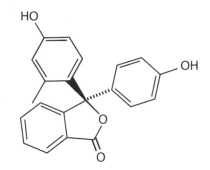

Figure 3 Structure of phenolphthalein

How to Titrate

1. Control the stopcock with one hand while you swirl the flask with the other hand.
2. Continue to titrate by adding the NaOH solution slowly until the light pink color lingers before disappearing; then add the NaOH by drops.
3. Stop titrating when the light pink color remains for at least 30 seconds; you have reached the end point.
4. If the pink color fades, add one more drop at a time until there is a change from colorless to a permanent pink.

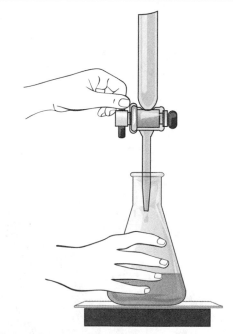

Figure 4 Titrating the unknown solution

6. Divide the grams of KHP by the molar mass (204.2 g/mol) to get the moles of KHP that reacted.

Assume that this number of moles of KHP equals the number of moles of NaOH reacted because the ions in KHP and NaOH react in a 1:1 ratio.

7. Divide the number of moles of NaOH reacted by the volume of solution containing it to get the molarity of NaOH for each trial. Show your work in the margin if needed.

---

8. Report the average molarity of NaOH on the basis of the values that you calculated for each trial. Show your work in the margin if needed.

⓾ Refill the buret with NaOH solution for the next part of the lab.

Titrating the Vinegar

❶ Pour about 55 mL of vinegar into a clean, dry 150 mL beaker.

❷ Thoroughly clean a second buret as you did the first one in step ❸ at the top of page 158, and rinse it out twice with a few milliliters of vinegar, including the tip. Place the buret in the clamp.

❸ Fill the buret with vinegar to about the 35 mL mark. Be sure to fill the tip by opening the stopcock for a moment. Record the initial volume in the buret to the nearest 0.01 mL in the Trial 1 column of Table 2.

❹ Allow about 3 mL of the vinegar to drain into a clean 250 mL Erlenmeyer flask. (It need not be dry.) Add about 20 mL of distilled water and two drops of phenolphthalein indicator to the vinegar in the flask.

9. Why is there a need to add water to the vinegar/phenolphthalein solution? (*Hint*: What will you be observing?)

---

❺ Record the initial volume in the NaOH buret to the nearest 0.01 mL in Table 2.

❻ Titrate the vinegar in the flask with the NaOH solution from the buret. (See the margin note on "How to Titrate" on the previous page.)

❼ If you feel like you've added more than barely the amount needed to titrate the solution, add a few drops of vinegar from the buret and then carefully add NaOH until one drop causes the color to change to pink. Read and record the final volumes in the NaOH and vinegar burets to the nearest 0.01 mL in Table 2.

10. Write the reaction between sodium hydroxide and acetic acid to produce sodium acetate and water.

name _____

_____

❽ Repeat the titration in steps ❸ through ❼ with a second sample of vinegar. Be sure to read the volumes in the burets before the titration and after the titration to the nearest 0.01 mL, and record them in the Trial 2 column of Table 2.

❾ Rinse out your burets, including the tips, using several rinses with tap water, followed by a final rinse with distilled water.

❿ Calculate the amounts of NaOH and vinegar used in both trials and record them in Table 2.

Using the molarity and volume of the NaOH and the volume of the vinegar, you can calculate the molarity of the acetic acid in vinegar according to the formula below, which is valid only because acetic acid and NaOH react in a 1:1 mole ratio.

$$M_{vinegar} \times V_{vinegar} = M_{NaOH} \times V_{NaOH}$$

11. Calculate the molarity of the vinegar (acetic acid) for each trial using the formula above. Show your work in the margin if needed.

_____

12. Report the average molarity of acetic acid on basis of the values that you calculated for each trial. Show your work in the margin if needed.

_____

From this molarity of vinegar, you will then be able to calculate the percent by mass of acetic acid in white vinegar. Using the molarity of acetic acid in vinegar and the molar mass of acetic acid ($HC_2H_3O_2$, 60.1 g/mol), you can determine the mass of acetic acid in a measured volume of vinegar. Assuming the density of vinegar to be 1.01 g/mL, you can then find the mass of the vinegar sample and thus the percent by mass.

13. Calculate the percent acetic acid in your vinegar by mass.

_____

14. Check your bottle of vinegar. How does this compare with what the label says?

_____

_____

_____

You can see that scientists titrate something you eat, just like the lactic acid in the whey of cheese. There are other uses of titration, including the production of biodiesel, aquarium water testing, and medical analysis of medication levels in IV drips or the glucose levels of diabetic patients.

15. How does titration play a role in helping people solve real-world problems in these uses?

_____

_____

_____

_____

_____

Table 1		
	Trial 1	Trial 2
Initial volume of NaOH (mL)		
Mass of flask		
Mass of flask and $KHC_3H_4O_4$		
Mass of $KHC_3H_4O_4$		
Final volume of NaOH		
Volume of NaOH used		

Table 2		
	Trial 1	Trial 2
Initial volume of vinegar		
Initial volume of NaOH		
Final volume of NaOH		
Final volume of vinegar		
Volume of vinegar used		
Volume of NaOH used		

17 OXIDATION AND REDUCTION

17A THE DEAD, TWITCHING FROG MYSTERY

The Voltaic Cell

A whole new world opened to chemists in the late 1790s with the discovery of electrochemistry. When Alessandro Volta built the first battery, he probably didn't realize how significant his invention was. Volta created the battery to settle a dispute that he was having with fellow scientist Luigi Galvani. Galvani had noticed that a freshly dissected frog leg would twitch when he touched it with two strips of different metals joined at one end. He believed that this experiment demonstrated the existence of what he called "animal electricity"—electricity generated by a biological system.

Volta disagreed with Galvani's interpretation of his experiment. Instead, Volta believed that the electricity originated because of the dissimilar metals. He constructed a number of simple batteries to confirm that biological material was not needed. One example appears in Figure 1. As you can see, it's made from a series of cups containing an electrolytic solution and connected by strips of two different metals. In reality, both men were partially correct. Volta was right in that the metals were the key to what Galvani had observed. But Galvani was correct in believing that biological tissues *can* generate electricity. Neither, however, understood the essential role that an electrolyte played in the overall picture.

Volta's battery started a revolution in chemistry. Scientists used it to isolate elements, to plate metals, and to power machines, as well as to expand their understanding of matter, electricity, and chemical reactions. Let's take a look at Volta's battery to expand our understanding of redox reactions, the chemistry that makes it work.

name _____

section _____ date _____

Figure 1 One of Volta's batteries, known as a "crown of cups"

PROCEDURE

Setting Up

❶ Fill the beaker with approximately 40 mL of acetic acid.

❷ Connect the alligator clip leads to the multimeter's probes. Switch the meter on and set it to measure DC voltage.

❸ Form the mechanical pencil leads into a bundle, using a small piece of tape in the middle to secure them. They will act as a carbon *electrode*. Gently connect the alligator clip lead coming from the positive (+) multimeter probe (usually red) to the top of the bundle.

Why Carbon?

Carbon is often used as an electrode because it is fairly unreactive and also inexpensive. If the electrode itself participates in a chemical reaction of its own, it can distort the data from the reaction that is being studied. Scientists also use platinum electrodes for the same purpose, but since platinum can cost over a thousand dollars per ounce, you can see why carbon is an attractive alternative!

What's Voltage?

Everyone's heard of voltage, but most people don't really know what it is. It's simply a measurement of the difference between two regions that have an electrical charge. Charged regions can be thought of as having potential energy relative to each other. The difference between them represents the potential to do work by moving charges. For example, an ordinary D-cell battery (like the one in a large flashlight) has a positive charge at one end and a negative charge at the other. Because the ends are different, they have the potential to do work when connected in a circuit (a complete electrical path). Voltage is simply the measurement of the *potential difference*. In the case of the D-cell battery, the difference is 1.5 V. As you may have guessed, the unit of voltage—the *volt*—is named in honor of Alessandro Volta.

Testing Metals

❶ Using the sandpaper, rub the zinc strip so that it brightens, and then clip it to the alligator lead connected to the negative (–) multimeter probe (usually black).

1. Why is it important to clean the metal with sandpaper before performing the experiment?

_____

_____

❷ Dip the carbon and zinc electrodes in the acetic acid, making sure that they don't touch. As soon as the multimeter gives a clear voltage reading, record this value to the nearest 0.01 V in the appropriate row of Table 1. Generally, the voltage will start to drop within just a few seconds, so read the meter quickly.

❸ Repeat steps ❶ and ❷ using the magnesium strip in place of the zinc.

2. What did you observe happening around the magnesium strip during the procedure?

_____

_____

3. Is what you observed in Question 2 part of the voltaic cell reaction that you're measuring, or is it an independent chemical reaction?

_____

_____

4. How could you experimentally arrive at an answer to Question 3?

_____

_____

_____

_____

❹ Use the procedure that you outlined in Question 4 to find an answer to Question 3.

5. What did you conclude in step ❹? Explain.

_____

_____

_____

_____

❺ Connect a single alligator clip lead between the carbon and zinc electrodes (see Figure 2). The meter will not be used.

❻ Immerse the two electrodes in the acetic acid, making sure that they don't touch. Leave the setup undisturbed for 10 minutes. Answer Questions 6–13 while you wait.

As you can guess, a voltaic cell involves a redox reaction. But the question is, what is oxidizing and what is reducing? The following equations describe the reaction for the first experiment (zinc electrode).

$$Zn\ (s) \longrightarrow Zn^{2+}\ (aq) + 2e^-$$

$$2H^+\ (aq) + 2e^- \longrightarrow H_2\ (g)$$

6. What's happening in the first reaction? How do you know?

_____

_____

_____

_____

7. Where is the zinc going? How do you know?

_____

_____

_____

8. Where are the electrons going? How do you know?

_____

_____

_____

9. Using your answer to Question 8, describe what is happening electrically to the zinc electrode.

_____

_____

10. If this process goes on long enough, what do you expect to happen to the zinc electrode?

_____

_____

11. What's happening in the second reaction? How do you know?

_____

_____

_____

_____

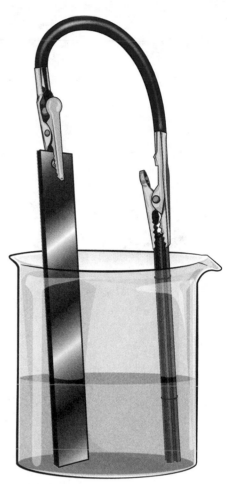

Figure 2 The setup for the voltaic cell

12. Where are the hydrogen ions in the second equation coming from?

_____

_____

13. What do you expect to see happening as a consequence of the second reaction?

_____

_____

❼ After 10 minutes has elapsed, carefully examine both electrodes in good light. *Do not touch or jiggle them!*

14. What do you observe?

_____

_____

15. Describe in detail what you think is happening when you connect the electrodes together and immerse them in the acid.

_____

_____

_____

_____

_____

_____

_____

_____

_____

16. Does the carbon electrode undergo a redox reaction? Explain.

_____

_____

_____

_____

17. What role do you think the carbon electrode plays in the voltaic cell?

_____

_____

_____

Comparing Voltages

When you measured the voltages developed by the zinc and magnesium, you may have wondered why they were different. There must be something about the metal that affects the reaction. Volta and other scientists observed that batteries made from different metals performed differently. Eventually, scientists figured out a way to classify different materials to predict how they would behave in a battery.

Each substance to be tested is placed in a voltaic cell (Figure 3) containing an electrolyte of a standard molarity (1 *M*), at a specific temperature (25 °C), and at a specific atmospheric pressure (1 atm). The second electrode is made from a glass tube containing hydrogen gas. The hydrogen gas is treated as a *standard reference electrode* and is assumed to have a value of 0 V. The voltage between the hydrogen electrode and the material being tested is measured. Since the hydrogen is treated as 0, the relative voltage difference between the two points is considered to be the material's specific voltage value. These values are published as a table of *standard electrode potentials*, which is commonly found in most chemistry reference texts.

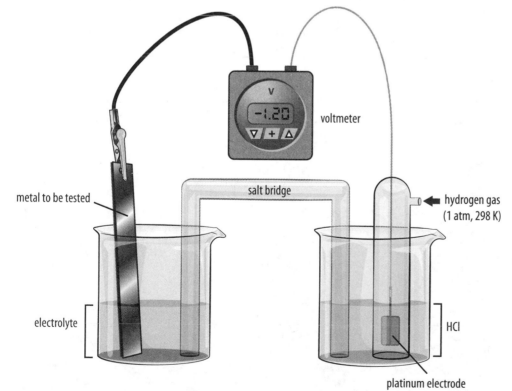

Figure 3 Apparatus used to determine standard electrode potentials

❶ The standard electrode potentials for zinc and magnesium are shown in the last column of Table 1. Compare these to the values that you measured and recorded in the table.

18. Ignoring the sign on the standard values, do you think the measured values reflect the general trend shown by the standard values?

_____

19. Are the measured values reasonably close to the standard values?

_____

20. If they are *not* reasonably close, can you think of possible reasons to account for the difference?

_____

_____

_____

_____

_____

_____

_____

Table 1		
Material	**Measured voltage (V)**	**Standard electrode potential (V)**
Zinc (Zn)		−0.76
Magnesium (Mg)		−2.37

17B Danger Under the Sink
Oxidation-Reduction Titration

name _____

section _____ date _____

Almost daily, poison control experts hear of people who are injured when they mix cleaning chemicals. One of the major culprits is bleach, a chemical you probably have under your kitchen sink or in the cabinet above your washing machine.

Bleach, a solution of sodium hypochlorite (NaClO), can react with other chemicals to produce chlorine gas (Cl_2). This gas is poisonous and can injure respiratory passages when inhaled. So how does the chlorine in bleach turn into chlorine gas? It's a redox reaction.

In this reaction, chlorine loses electrons (is oxidized) to form chlorine gas. This kind of reaction can help us know something about the concentration of the original reactant, in this case, the sodium hypochlorite solution. Using a reaction to do this is similar to an acid-base titration. These titrations use an indicator to show when the acid and base reach an end point, near which the pH is neutral.

In this lab, you will do a redox titration to find out the concentration of a potassium permanganate solution ($KMnO_4$). Potassium permanganate is also used to clean the filters of pools. But you won't need an indicator for this titration—the potassium permanganate acts as its own indicator! As this redox titration reaches its end point, you will watch the solution change color, similar to the color change of phenolphthalein.

Figure 1 Chlorine gas injures respiratory passages as it reacts with water there to form hydrochloric acid. It was one of the first chemicals to be used for chemical warfare.

Objectives
✓ Review the technique of titration.
✓ Determine the concentration of an oxidizer using the technique of titration.
✓ Track the movement of electrons in a redox titration.

Equipment
laboratory scale (accurate to 0.01 g)
beaker, 150 mL
buret, 50 mL
buret clamp
Erlenmeyer flask, 125 mL
filtering funnel
graduated cylinder, 10 mL
graduated cylinder, 100 mL
ring stand
potassium permanganate solution ($KMnO_4$)
iron (II) sulfate heptahydrate ($FeSO_4 \cdot 7H_2O$)
sulfuric acid (H_2SO_4), 6 M

PROCEDURE
Setting Up

❶ Add about 60 mL of $KMnO_4$ solution to a clean, dry 150 mL beaker.

❷ Attach the buret clamp to the ring stand.

❸ Thoroughly clean the buret by rinsing it with water several times. Then rinse it twice with a few milliliters of the $KMnO_4$ solution. Be sure to rinse the tip as well, allowing solution to drain out of the buret. Then place the buret in the clamp as shown in Figure 2.

1. Record your observations of the $KMnO_4$ solution.

_____

_____

Figure 2 Redox titration setup

❹ Close the stopcock and, with the aid of a funnel, carefully fill the buret with $KMnO_4$ solution. Open the stopcock and drain out some of the solution until the tip of the buret is filled. Add $KMnO_4$ solution to the buret, if necessary, until the level of the liquid is near but not above 0 mL. Record the initial volume to the nearest 0.01 mL in the Trial 1 column of Table 1.

❺ Determine the mass of the 150 mL Erlenmeyer flask to the nearest 0.01 g. (It need not be dry inside.) Record this value in Table 1.

❻ Add about 0.70 g of iron (II) sulfate ($FeSO_4$) to the flask on the scale. Record the combined weight to the nearest 0.01 g in Table 1.

❼ Use this information to calculate the mass and the moles of $FeSO_4$ used. Record these results in Table 1.

2. Write a chemical equation for the reaction of permanganate ions with iron (II) ions to form manganese and iron (III) ions. Don't be concerned with balancing the elements in this equation for now.

_____

3. Why are the potassium and sulfate ions not included in this reaction? (*Hint*: Review net ionic equations on pages 214 and 216 of your textbook.)

_____

_____

4. Which is the oxidizing agent?

_____

5. What happens to iron?

_____

6. Which is the reducing agent?

_____

7. What happens to manganese?

_____

❽ Add 10 mL of distilled water to the flask, and swirl the flask until all the solid iron (II) sulfate dissolves. Use a few milliliters of water from a wash bottle to wash any crystals that cling to the wall of the flask down into the solution.

❾ Add 1 mL of 6 M H_2SO_4 solution (sulfuric acid) to the flask.

8. What does the sulfuric acid add to the solution that affects the redox reaction? (*Hint*: Think about redox reactions as the movement of electrons.)

_____

_____

Now you're ready to titrate!

Titrating KMnO₄

❶ Place the flask on a piece of white paper under the buret. You'll use this to help you see when the color in the flask starts changing. Lower the buret until the tip extends into the flask.

❷ Titrate the $FeSO_4$ solution by adding a few milliliters of $KMnO_4$ from the buret as you swirl the flask to mix the solutions (see Figure 3). Stop adding $KMnO_4$ when the light pink color doesn't go away with swirling. Read the final volume in the buret to the nearest 0.01 mL and record it in Table 1.

❸ Calculate the amount of $KMnO_4$ used in the titration and record it in Table 1.

❹ Now you'll do Trial 2. As you did in step ❹ on the previous page, add $KMnO_4$ solution to the buret until the level of the liquid is near but not above 0 mL. Record this initial volume to the nearest 0.01 mL in the Trial 2 column of Table 1.

❺ Make a new sample of iron (II) sulfate solution as you did in steps ❺ through ❾ on the previous page. Record the relevant data in the Trial 2 column of Table 1. Make sure that you rinse out your flask well before making the new $FeSO_4$ solution.

❻ Do another titration of this new $FeSO_4$ solution as you did in step ❷ above. Record your data in Table 1.

❼ Calculate the amount of $KMnO_4$ used in the titration and record it in Table 1.

❽ Drain any unreacted potassium permanganate solution from your buret into a waste beaker that your teacher provides.

9. Describe the color change that you observed as you did the titration.

_____

_____

_____

_____

_____

The balanced redox equation for the reaction of potassium permanganate and iron (II) sulfate is shown below.

$$2KMnO_4 + 8H_2SO_4 + 10FeSO_4 \longrightarrow$$
$$K_2SO_4 + 2MnSO_4 + 5Fe_2(SO_4)_3 + 8H_2O$$

This might make a little more sense if you look at what is happening to the ions.

$$2MnO_4^- + 16H^+ + 10Fe^{2+} \longrightarrow 2Mn^{2+} + 8H_2O + 10Fe^{3+}$$

10. What happens to the oxygens in the permanganate ion?

_____

_____

How to Titrate

1. Control the stopcock with one hand while you swirl the flask with the other hand.

2. Continue to titrate by adding the $KMnO_4$ solution slowly until the light pink color lingers before disappearing; then add the $KMnO_4$ by drops.

3. Stop titrating when the light pink color remains for at least 30 seconds; you have reached the end point.

4. If the pink color fades, add one more drop at a time until there is a change from colorless to a permanent pink.

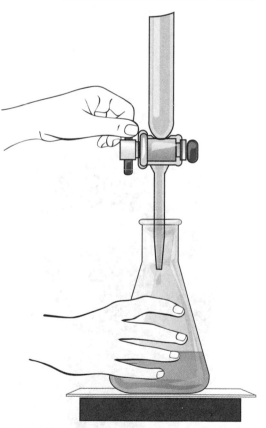

Figure 3 This is how you titrate the $FeSO_4$ solution.

Using the grams of $FeSO_4$ that you measured into the solution and the volume of $KMnO_4$ solution needed to react with all of it, you can calculate the molarity of the $KMnO_4$ solution.

11. Divide the grams of $FeSO_4$ by the molar mass to get the moles of $FeSO_4$ that reacted.

_____

12. Use the ratio of moles of Fe^{2+} to the number of moles of MnO_4^- from the ion equation to find the moles of permanganate that reacted. This is the same as the moles of $KMnO_4$ that reacted.

_____

13. Divide the number of moles of MnO_4^- ($KMnO_4$) that reacted by the volume of solution containing it to get the molarity of $KMnO_4$ for each trial. Show your work in the margin if needed.

_____

14. Report the average molarity of $KMnO_4$ using the values that you calculated for each trial. Show your work in the margin if needed.

_____

15. Get the actual concentration of the potassium permanganate solution from your teacher and calculate a percent error.

_____

16. Potassium permanganate is used for medical purposes such as treating skin diseases and infections. On the basis of what you have observed in this lab, suggest some reasons why.

_____

_____

_____

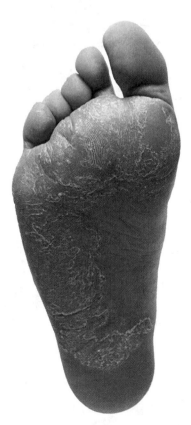

Figure 4 Potassium permanganate can be used to treat fungal infections such as athlete's foot. Dilute solutions of potassium permanganate are used in footbaths.

Table 1		
	Trial 1	Trial 2
Initial volume of $KMnO_4$ solution		
Mass of flask		
Mass of flask and $FeSO_4$		
Mass of $FeSO_4$		
Moles of $FeSO_4$		
Final volume of $KMnO_4$ solution		
Volume of $KMnO_4$ solution used		

18 ORGANIC CHEMISTRY AND BIOCHEMISTRY

18A MAKES SCENTS!

Synthesizing Esters

An Indian farmer wielding a machete approaches a tree with large leaves. He's headed for a cluster of green fruit with a slightly yellow tint. The smell of ripe bananas invites him to harvest their starchy goodness. Time for bananas!

The smell that bananas make is a naturally produced ester called *isoamyl acetate*. This ester can be synthesized in labs to be used for everything from banana-flavored chewing gum to solvents for varnishes and lacquers. This chemical also has the very convenient ability to attract large numbers of honeybees—a good trick for the banana tree!

Smaller esters such as isoamyl acetate have an attractive scent. They form when an alcohol reacts with a carboxylic acid. The hydrogen from the alcohol reacts with the hydroxyl group on the carboxylic acid to form water.

$$R - C \overset{O}{\underset{O-H}{\big\backslash}} + R'OH \rightleftharpoons R - C \overset{O}{\underset{O-R'}{\big\backslash}} + H_2O$$

In this lab, you'll get to make some chemicals that actually smell good! You'll mix three different combinations of carboxylic acids and alcohols to form three different esters. Let's make some scents of esters!

name _____

section _____ date _____

Objectives

✓ Predict the esters produced from carboxylic acids and alcohols.

✓ Observe the production of esters from carboxylic acids and alcohols.

Equipment

laboratory thermometer
test tubes (3)
test tube holder
beakers, 50 mL (3)
beaker, 250 mL
pipets (3)
sulfuric acid, concentrated
methanol
ethanol
isopropanol
acetic acid
salicylic acid
sodium bicarbonate ($NaHCO_3$) solution
grease pencil or masking tape

Figure 1 Banana trees aren't actually trees at all; they are plants with a tall stem that acts like a tree trunk. Banana trees are the largest flower-producing plants in the world.

PROCEDURE

Setting Up

❶ Label three 50 mL beakers with the numbers 1, 2, and 3, and fill each half full with water. You will be using these beakers of water to help you observe the smell of the esters that you produce.

❷ Label three clean, dry test tubes 1–3.

1. In the reaction above, what do the R and R′ represent?

_____

_____

You will be adding sulfuric acid to the mixtures of carboxylic acids and alcohols and then heating these mixtures.

2. Keeping in mind that this is an equilibrium reaction, what do you think is the purpose for adding heat and acid?

_____

_____

You will be putting carboxylic acid and alcohol pairs into the test tubes as follows:

Tube 1: salicylic acid and methanol

Tube 2: acetic acid and ethanol

Tube 3: acetic acid and isopropanol

3. What is R and R′ for salicylic acid and methanol? See the structure of salicylic acid below.

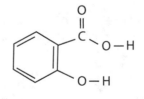

_____

4. Write a reaction predicting the result of combining salicylic acid and methanol.

_____

❸ Name the ester produced in this reaction, and record it in the Tube 1 row of Table 1.

5. What is R and R′ for acetic acid and ethanol?

_____

6. Write a reaction predicting the result of combining acetic acid and ethanol.

_____

❹ Name the ester produced in this reaction, and record it in the Tube 2 row of Table 1.

7. What is R and R′ for acetic acid and isopropanol?

_____

8. Write a reaction predicting the result of combining acetic acid and isopropanol.

_____

❺ Name the ester produced in this reaction, and record it in the Tube 3 row of Table 1.

Now you're ready to make some esters!

Cooking Up Some Esters

❶ Fill the 250 mL beaker half full with hot tap water. Heat it in a microwave to about 70 °C, *but no warmer.*

❷ In Tube 1, add 0.50 g salicylic acid. To this, add 20 drops of methanol.

❸ In Tube 2, add 10 drops of acetic acid and 20 drops of ethanol.

❹ In Tube 3, add 10 drops of acetic acid and 20 drops of isopropanol.

❺ Now add 2 drops of concentrated sulfuric acid to each tube. The sulfuric acid acts as a catalyst to help speed up the reaction between the alcohol and the carboxylic acid. Swirl to mix the contents of each tube.

❻ Put all three test tubes into the hot water. Let them sit in the water *for about five minutes.* If the contents of a test tube begin to boil, raise the test tube out of the hot water with a test tube holder, and then return it to the hot water bath when boiling stops.

❼ Let the test tubes cool. Add 10–20 drops of sodium bicarbonate ($NaHCO_3$) solution until the contents of the tube stop fizzing (about 1 mL).

❽ Then pour the contents of each test tube into the beaker that corresponds to it (Tube 1 gets poured into Beaker 1, for example).

❾ Waft the aroma of the liquid in each beaker toward your nose (see Figure 2), and describe what you observe in Table 1. You may want to waft the aromas of the carboxylic acids and alcohols to contrast the smells. ***Do not put your nose directly over the containers while smelling.***

> ⚠ **No Flames!**
>
> The chemicals you are working with in this lab are highly flammable, so make sure that there are no laboratory burners turned on during this lab.

Figure 2 Carefully observe the aroma of the solutions in the beakers!

Figure 3 Polyester, which is used in fabrics and rope casings, is a long chain of esters.

9. What kinds of products would esters be useful for? Explain your answer.

_____

_____

_____

10. Where would the esters to make these products come from, and how could chemistry help?

_____

_____

_____

_____

_____

	Carboxylic acid	Alcohol	Ester	Observations
Tube 1	salicylic acid	methanol		
Tube 2	acetic acid	ethanol		
Tube 3	acetic acid	isopropanol		

Table 1

18B MILKING CHEMISTRY
Proteins in Food

name _____

section _____ date _____

In the desolate, frozen plains of Antarctica, a group of male emperor penguins huddles in the brutal winds and isolating darkness of polar winter. And yet, under the downy folds of these penguins lies a solitary egg, soon to hatch to reveal an emperor chick to this seemingly inhospitable world. But where will his first meal come from? All the emperor mothers are back at the coast, gorging on fish to recover from laying their eggs while the males protect the eggs.

But these feathered fathers have a trick up the sleeves of their tuxedoes! Emperor penguins, flamingos, pigeons, and doves can produce something called *crop milk*. Though not the same as the milk that mammals produce, this milk is also high in protein, just what chicks need to get a good start on life. This milk comes from a lining inside the bird's mouths that stores partially digested food. The father regurgitates this food to feed to his chick.

Objectives

✓ Detect the presence of proteins and peptides in foods.

✓ Explain the difference between peptides and proteins.

✓ Explain how the biuret test works.

Equipment

test tubes (6)

test tube rack

transfer pipet (eyedropper)

copper (II) sulfate solution ($CuSO_4$), 2%

sodium hydroxide (NaOH), 6 *M*

milk, fresh and fermented

albumin (from egg whites)

Optional (see page 179)

laboratory scale (accurate to 0.01 g)

beaker, 150 mL

mortar and pestle

acetone

sand

food to be tested

test tubes, labeled (2)

Figure 1 Male emperor penguins produce crop milk to sustain chicks until their mothers return from the coast to feed them regurgitated fish.

Carbohydrates, proteins, and fats make up the bulk of the biomolecules found in the foods that sustain animals and people. Cow's milk—what some people consider a complete food—contains all three of these groups.

You've been learning about proteins—large molecules made of amino acids chemically linked together by *peptide bonds*. The major protein in cow's milk is *casein*, but it also contains the proteins *albumin* and *globulin*. Albumin is a protein also found in egg whites.

Protein is an important part of our diet. Our bodies need proteins and the amino acids they contain to function properly. We naturally make some amino acids, but not all that we need. We must get the rest from the food we consume. Beans, fish, poultry, beef, seeds, nuts, and whole grains are all high in protein. In this lab, you will use a combination of chemicals to detect proteins in foods, including milk.

Keeping the Tubes Straight

The contents for each test tube:

1: 6 *M* NaOH

2: 2% CuSO₄ solution

3: fresh milk

4: fermented milk

5: egg albumin

6: water

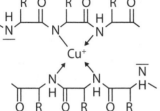

Figure 2 The copper chelate that forms during the biuret test for proteins

Don't Be Fooled!

Don't mistake the deepening of the blue color for a color change to violet. A blue color is a negative result for the biuret test of proteins.

PROCEDURE

The Protein Test

❶ Label six clean test tubes with the numbers 1–6.

❷ Fill each test tube about 1/3 full with (in this order) NaOH solution, CuSO₄ solution, fresh milk, fermented milk, egg albumin, and water.

Next, you'll be combining two chemicals with the contents of each of these tubes. These two chemicals, 6 *M* NaOH solution and 2% CuSO₄ solution, work together to test for proteins in what is called the *biuret test*.

1. Suggest what the NaOH does to amino acids in proteins. (*Hint:* Think of the name *amino acid*.)

_____

_____

After the sodium hydroxide does its work, the copper (II) sulfate hops into the protein, replacing the peptide bond with a structure called a *chelate* (see Figure 2). In this chelate, the lone pairs on four nitrogens bond with the Cu^{2+} ion. The chelate makes the color change to violet or pinkish violet.

2. What kind of bond forms between the nitrogen and copper atoms?

_____

3. Why is the nitrogen able to form a bond with the copper?

_____

_____

4. How do you think a biuret test could be used to find out how much protein is in a food?

_____

_____

5. Is the biuret test a qualitative or quantitative test? Explain.

_____

_____

❸ To Tubes 3–6, add 5 drops of 6 *M* NaOH from Tube 1 and 3 drops of 2% copper (II) sulfate solution from Tube 2.

❹ Mix each tube by agitating it. Allow the tubes to stand for 3–5 minutes.

❺ Record your observations of color and protein presence from the biuret test in Table 1.

Sometimes the biuret test produces a pinkish color change or a faint purple color. This happens when there are peptides present. So what's the difference between a peptide and a protein? Peptides involve fewer amino acids, as few as two. Proteins consist of several peptide chains that coil into complex shapes. They can involve hundreds of amino acids. So proteins are chemically similar to peptides—just bigger!

6. What did you notice in the results of the tests of fresh milk and fermented milk?

_____

_____

7. Why do you think this happened?

_____

_____

_____

_____

Testing Other Foods (Optional)

You can test more food for the presence of proteins!

❶ For solid food, weigh out a 2 g sample and grind it into small pieces with a mortar and pestle. (List the foods that you are testing in Table 1.)

❷ Add about 5 mL of acetone and allow the mixture to settle for several minutes. Decant the liquid into a 150 mL beaker and set it aside.

❸ Add 1–2 g of clean sand to the residue in the mortar and continue grinding the food as you gradually add 10–15 mL of distilled water. Grind thoroughly until you have a well-pulverized suspension.

❹ Decant the suspension into the same 150 mL beaker, leaving the sediment behind. Add the suspension to a labeled test tube.

❺ For liquid food, simply fill a labeled test tube about 1/3 full.

❻ Add 5 drops of 6 M NaOH and 3 drops of 2% copper (II) sulfate solution.

❼ Mix each tube by agitating it. Allow the tubes to stand for 3–5 minutes.

❽ Record your observations of color and protein presence from the biuret test in Table 1.

Check the nutrition labels of the foods that you tested for the presence of protein.

8. Describe your success in detecting proteins using the biuret test.

_____

_____

9. Describe any observations of variation in color or color intensity that you observed.

_____

_____

10. Compare the amounts of protein on the nutrition labels of the foods that you tested to the intensity of the purple color that you observed.

_____

_____

11. Record any patterns that you observed in the foods that demonstrated a positive biuret test.

_____

_____

_____

12. From a chemistry standpoint, what does a negative biuret test signify?

_____

_____

13. Do some research on proteins in diet. Describe the importance of proteins in your diet.

_____

_____

_____

14. Why is it important for a Christian to maintain a healthy diet?

_____

_____

_____

Figure 3 Eating a variety of foods that is chemically diverse is important for sustaining a healthy body.

Table 1		
	Color observed	Protein present?
Fresh milk		
Fermented milk		
Egg albumin		
Water		

19 MATERIALS CHEMISTRY

19 A PLASTIC WORLD
Inquiring into Plastics

name _____

section _____   date _____

Imagine a world without plastic. Things would weigh more, cost more, and sometimes break sooner! Imagine how different the car industry and the medical industry would be if we didn't have plastics. Just look around you right now—your clothing, shoes, chair, pen, smartphone, and even the building you are in rely on the materials chemistry of plastics.

We live in a world full of plastic. But not all plastic is the same. Its properties vary widely, as do its uses. Some plastics are hard and rigid while others are very flexible; some melt easily while others resist high temperatures; and some are transparent while others are opaque or translucent. Some tear easily, and some resist tearing. Their uses range from car parts to the clothing we wear, from food and beverage containers to utensils used for eating, and from grocery bags to shampoo bottles. Their uses often stem from their physical properties, which, in turn, are a result of their chemical structure.

Because traditional plastics don't react and break down very quickly, a greater emphasis has recently been placed on recycling plastics instead of burning them or putting them in landfills. Some are recycled by being used in a totally different application; others are melted down and reused in similar or identical ways; and some are not recyclable. Scientists have also been developing and using biodegradable plastics. There are so many types of plastics in use, and since different methods of recycling are used for each, they need to be separated from one another according to type.

Objectives

✓ Determine the relative densities of plastics to aid in their identification.
✓ Identify the type of plastic in an unknown plastic sample.

Equipment

laboratory burner and lighter
beakers, 50 mL (4)
tweezers (or crucible tongs)
copper wire, 5 in.
cork, large
corn oil
isopropyl alcohol solution, 45.5%
plastic samples
salt water (NaCl), saturated
felt-tip pen
masking tape or grease pencil
marker, fine-tip, permanent ink (optional)

Figure 1 How many things can you find in this picture that are made of plastic?

In this lab, you will use density as the principal method to differentiate between the six common types of plastic, shown in Table 1. You'll also use a flame test to find out what is in the plastics. And you will use what you learn from known samples of plastic to identify an unknown sample of plastic.

Table 1			
Recycling number	Abbreviation	Polymer name	Density (g/cm³)
1	PET	polyethylene terephthalate	1.38–1.39
2	HDPE	high-density polyethylene	0.94–0.96
3	PVC	polyvinyl chloride	1.32–1.42
4	LDPE	low-density polyethylene	0.91–0.93
5	PP	polypropylene	0.90–0.92
6	PS	polystyrene	1.03–1.06

PROCEDURE

Density Tests

❶ Your teacher will supply you with one sample of each type of plastic. If they are not easily distinguishable from one another, make small identifying numbers or letters, using the felt-tip pen provided.

❷ Describe the physical appearance of the different samples of plastics in the first column of Table 2.

1. Do you think color is an accurate way to identify types of plastics? Why or why not?

_____

_____

❸ Now label four 50 mL beakers with the labels "water," "alcohol," "salt water," and "corn oil." Fill each beaker mostly full with the appropriate solution.

2. What can you conclude about the density of a plastic sample, compared to the liquid it is in, by its buoyancy?

_____

_____

_____

3. How could you use a variety of liquids to identify the densities of your plastic samples?

_____

_____

4. Order the plastic types in Table 1 by increasing density.

_____

Use the density information provided in the margin box to answer the questions below.

❹ Place all the plastic samples in the beaker for the liquid that you are testing, and stir with a stirring rod to overcome surface tension and to dislodge any air bubbles from the samples.

❺ Note which plastic samples float and which sink in the different liquids and record your observations in Table 2. (Be sure to wash and dry all your samples between tests of each liquid.)

5. If a plastic sample floated in salt water but sank in pure water, what does that tell you about its density?

_____

_____

6. If a plastic sample floated in pure water but sank in corn oil, what does that tell you about its density?

_____

_____

7. If a plastic sample floated in corn oil but sank in alcohol, what does that tell you about its density?

_____

_____

8. If any plastics have densities that overlap, how would you be able to identify an unknown of one of these types?

_____

_____

❻ Using tweezers or tongs, remove all your samples from the liquids. Wash them with soapy water and dry them with a paper towel.

The Flame Test

You may have noticed that some of the plastic samples have densities that are too close to each other to tell apart from the density test alone. You can do a flame test on plastics to tell what is in them.

❶ Insert the copper wire into the cork to a depth of about 0.5 in.

❷ While holding the cork as a handle, heat the free end of the wire in a well-adjusted burner flame until it no longer gives a green color to the flame. While it is still hot, touch the end to one of the plastic samples. This will melt a small amount of the plastic onto the wire.

name _____

Liquid Densities
alcohol: 0.8 g/mL
corn oil: 0.9 g/mL
water: 1.0 g/mL
saturated salt water: 1.2 g/mL

Keeping Samples Straight
You may want to set your plastic samples on paper towels labeled "floated" and "sank" to help you keep your samples straight.

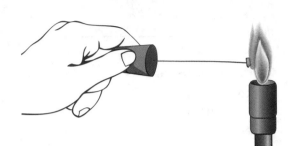

Figure 2 The copper wire flame test

⚠ Burning Plastic

Do not put the entire plastic sample in the flame! This could release large amounts of toxic smells.

What Do the Colors Mean?

Plastics that contain chlorine will produce a green flame; those that do not will burn with a yellow color.

9. Why did the flame turn green when you placed the wire in the flame? (*Hint*: Remember the lab on flame tests.)

_____

_____

❸ Now you will do a flame test on the plastic samples. (See Figure 2.) Insert the plastic-tinged wire again into the flame. Note the color produced and record it in the appropriate sample row of Table 2.

❹ Repeat step ❸ for each sample, being sure to burn off all of one sample before moving on to the next one. Record your observations in the appropriate sample rows of Table 2.

❺ Use the information in Table 1 and your observations in Table 2 to identify the plastic samples tested in the flame test.

10. Which plastics did the flame test help you identify that the density test could not?

_____

_____

11. How could it be helpful to do the flame test before the density tests for this group of plastic samples?

_____

_____

_____

Mystery Plastic

❶ Get a piece of unknown plastic sample from your teacher. You will use all the tests you just performed to identify what kind of plastic it is.

❷ Write a physical description of the unknown in Table 2.

❸ Do the density tests. Record what you observe in Table 2.

❹ Do the flame test. Record what you observe in Table 2.

❺ Dispose of the salt water, alcohol, and corn oil according to your teacher's instructions. Rinse the beakers well and allow them to drain thoroughly.

❻ Discard all the plastic samples in the trash and clean the oily beaker well with hot, soapy water.

12. Identify the type of plastic of the unknown. Explain your reasoning.

_____

_____

13. According to your observations, which plastic was the densest? Did this agree with the data in Table 1?

_____

14. Why was it necessary to use the copper wire test to distinguish one of the plastics from the others?

name _____

_____

_____

15. Why was it important to completely dry each piece of plastic between the different float tests?

_____

_____

16. Why is it important to be able to make and classify different types of plastics?

_____

_____

_____

_____

Table 2						
Plastic-ID	Physical description	Behavior in water	Behavior in alcohol solution	Behavior in salt water	Behavior in corn oil	Flame test
1-PET						
2-HDPE						
3-PVC						
4-LDPE						
5-PP						
6-PS						
Unknown						

20 NUCLEAR CHEMISTRY

20 ATOMIC ASTEROIDS
Mass Defect and Binding Energy

name _____

section _____   date _____

There are some asteroids that are essentially collections of rocks held together by the force of gravity alone. What would it take to break these asteroids apart, especially if one were on a collision course with Earth? The energy required would need to overcome the force of gravity.

Nuclides are like these asteroids in some ways. They are collections of subatomic particles held together with nuclear binding energy. Perhaps, just like these asteroids, it would take enough energy to overcome the binding energy for nuclides to undergo fission.

A fundamental idea of modern nuclear chemistry is that mass and energy are equivalent. Mass can be changed into energy, and energy can be changed into mass. The equivalence of mass and energy seems to be responsible for the force that holds a nucleus together. The equation $E = mc^2$ relates the quantities of mass and energy (where E is nuclear binding energy, m is the mass defect, and c is the speed of light). In nuclear reactions, a small amount of mass is converted into a large amount of energy. Again, the equation $E = mc^2$ describes the relationship between the quantities of mass and energy—E is the energy released, and m is the mass that is converted.

In this activity, you will calculate the binding energy per nuclear particle for He-4, Fe-56, and U-232 nuclides so that you can do a direct comparison of the energy packed into these nuclides. You will need to make several preliminary calculations for each atom. You might be surprised by which nuclides are the most stable!

PROCEDURE

❶ Find the total mass of all the electrons, protons, and neutrons for the three nuclides in Table 1. Add these masses together to find the total mass of nucleons for each nuclide. Assume that a proton is 1.0073 u, a neutron is 1.0087 u, and an electron is 0.000 55 u. Sodium-23 has been done as an example for you. Show your work in the margin if needed. Record the total mass of nucleons in Table 1.

Objectives

✓ Calculate the mass defect of given nuclides.

✓ Determine the binding energy per nucleon for given nuclei.

✓ Use the equation $E = mc^2$ in conversions between mass and energy.

Equipment

reference source (with precise masses of nuclides) or access to the Internet

Figure 1 Astronomers give the name *rubble piles* to asteroids that are loose collections of debris held together by gravity alone.

Sample Calculations for Na-23

Na-23 nuclides have 11 protons, 11 electrons, and 12 neutrons. Use the calculations below as a sample. Make sure that you follow the rules for significant digits.

Total mass of nucleons:

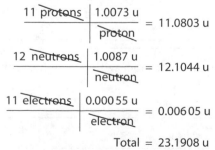

$$\frac{11 \text{ protons} \mid 1.0073 \text{ u}}{\text{proton}} = 11.0803 \text{ u}$$

$$\frac{12 \text{ neutrons} \mid 1.0087 \text{ u}}{\text{neutron}} = 12.1044 \text{ u}$$

$$\frac{11 \text{ electrons} \mid 0.000\,55 \text{ u}}{\text{electron}} = 0.006\,05 \text{ u}$$

Total = 23.1908 u

Mass defect:

For the Na-23 atom, the mass defect is the difference between the total mass of nucleons and the actual mass.

23.1908 u – 22.9898 u = 0.2010 u

1 u = 1.66×10^{-27} kg

The mass defect of the Na-23 atom is 3.34×10^{-28} kg.

Binding energy:

$E = mc^2$

$= (3.34 \times 10^{-28} \text{ kg})(3.00 \times 10^8 \text{ m/s})^2$

$= 3.01 \times 10^{-11} \text{ J}.$

Binding energy per particle:

The Na-23 atom has 23 nuclear particles; its binding energy per particle is

$$\frac{3.01 \times 10^{-11} \text{ J}}{23 \text{ particles}},$$

or 1.31×10^{-12} J/particle.

1. How do these masses compare to the atomic masses on the periodic table? Explain.

   _____

   _____

   _____

❷ Use reference books or the Internet to look up the actual masses of nuclides. This is different from the atomic masses on the periodic table. Record these in Table 1.

❸ To find the mass defect for an atom, subtract the actual mass from the total mass of nucleons. Calculate the mass defect for each isotope in atomic mass units, and record all three in Table 1.

2. Which atom of the three that you worked with in this activity had the greatest mass defect? Which had the least?

   _____

❹ Convert the mass defect to units of kilograms ($1\ u = 1.66 \times 10^{-27}\ kg$). Show your work in the margin if needed. Record these energy conversions in Table 1.

❺ Using $E = mc^2$, express the mass defect as the binding energy. When the mass defect is expressed in kilograms, and the speed of light is in meters per second, this equation yields the binding energy in joules (J). Record your calculations in Table 1.

3. Which atom had the greatest binding energy? Which had the least?

   _____

❻ Calculate the binding energy per nucleon by dividing the binding energy by the number of nucleons in the nucleus. Record your calculations in Table 1.

4. Which atom had the greatest binding energy per nucleon? Which had the least?

   _____

❼ Plot the binding energy per nucleon on the graphing area at the end of the lab for comparison to other nuclides. Connect them with a smooth curve.

5. Describe any general observations that you have about your graph.

   _____

   _____

   _____

6. Using your curve, estimate the mass number with the highest binding energy per nucleon.

   _____

   _____

7. Compare your graph with Figure 20-25 on page 545 of your text-book. What do you notice?

name _____

_____

_____

8. If a nuclide split apart, would the process release or absorb energy? Why?

_____

_____

_____

_____

_____

9. A 20-megaton hydrogen bomb releases energy equivalent to that of the explosion of 20 million tons of TNT, a powerful chemical explosive. Use the fact that 1 ton of TNT releases 4.184×10^9 joules of energy to calculate how much matter is converted into energy in the thermonuclear explosion. Show your work in the margin if needed.

_____

10. Would it be wrong to use a 20-megaton hydrogen bomb during war? Why or why not?

_____

_____

_____

_____

_____

_____

_____

_____

_____

Figure 2 This is what a hydrogen bomb looks like when it explodes. Lots of energy here!

Table 1	He-4	Na-23	Fe-56	U-232
Total mass of nucleons (u)		23.1908		
Actual mass (u)		22.9898		
Mass defect (u)		0.2010		
Mass defect (kg)		3.34×10^{-28}		
Binding energy (J)		3.01×10^{-11}		
Binding energy per nucleon (J/particle)		1.31×10^{-12}		

Binding Energy per Nucleon vs. Atomic Mass Number

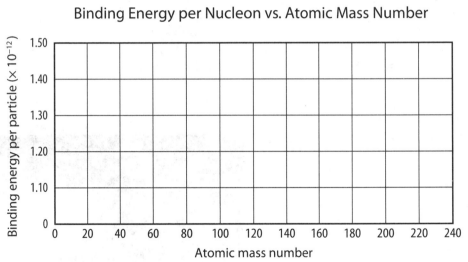

APPENDIX A
Lab and First-Aid Rules

LAB RULES

1. Never perform an unauthorized experiment or change any assigned experiment without your teacher's permission.

2. Avoid playful, distracting, or boisterous behavior.

3. Work at your own lab station.

4. Always wear safety goggles when working with chemicals and other objects that are potentially hazardous to the eyes.

5. Wear protective clothing and gloves when working with corrosive or staining chemicals.

6. While working in the lab, tie back long hair and avoid wearing loose clothing such as ties.

7. Never eat, drink, or chew gum in the lab.

8. Never taste any chemical or eat or drink out of glassware found in the lab.

9. To smell a substance, gently fan its vapor toward you.

10. Never leave a flame or heater unattended. Keep combustible materials away from sources of heat.

11. When diluting acid solutions, always add the acid to water slowly. Avoid adding water to an acid.

12. When heating a test tube, point the open end away from you. Never heat a closed or stoppered container.

13. Dispose of solid and liquid chemical waste as instructed by your teacher.

14. Do not return unused chemicals to a bottle. Dispose of them properly.

15. Notify the teacher of any injuries, spills, or breakages.

FIRST-AID RULES

1. **Burns**

   For burns from hot objects, flames, or chemicals, flush the area with cold water for several minutes.

2. **Chemical spills**

   a. On a laboratory desk

      1. If the material is not particularly volatile, toxic, or flammable, use an absorbent material that will soak up the liquid. Then clean the area with soap and water.

      2. If the material is volatile, flammable, or toxic, get your teacher for help unless it is a large spill. If it is a large spill, you may need to evacuate the lab.

      3. When highly reactive materials such as hydrochloric acid are spilled, the teacher will clean them up.

b. On a person

1. If the spill covers a large area, remove all contaminated clothing while under the safety shower. Flood the affected body area for fifteen minutes. Obtain medical help immediately.

2. If the spill covers a small area, immediately flush the affected area with cold water for several minutes. Then wash the area with a mild detergent solution.

3. If the spill is an acid, rinse the area with sodium bicarbonate solution; if it is a base, use boric acid solution.

4. If the chemical splashes in the eyes, immediately wash the eyes in the nearest eyewash fountain for several minutes. Get medical attention.

3. **Fire**

a. For any fire other than a contained fire, don't attempt to put it out on your own. Some fires can't be put out with water.

b. Smother a small fire in a container by covering it.

c. If a person's clothes are on fire, roll the person on the floor and use a fire blanket to extinguish the flames. The safety shower may also be used. ***Do not use a fire extinguisher.***

4. **Swallowing chemicals**

Determine the specific substance ingested. Contact the Poison Control Center in your area immediately.

APPENDIX B
Laboratory Equipment

beaker

buret clamp

clay triangle

buret

crucible and cover

crucible tongs

filtering funnel

electronic scale

Erlenmeyer flask

evaporating dish

filter paper

iron ring

laboratory lighter

eye dropper

graduated cylinder

laboratory burner

ring stand

mortar and pestle

pinchcock clamp

rubber stoppers

plastic transfer pipet

spatula

test tube brush

test tube clamp

test tube

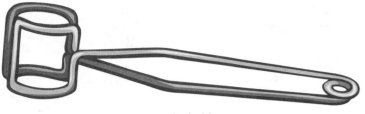

test tube holder

wash bottle

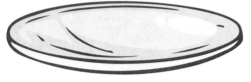

watch glass

weighing paper

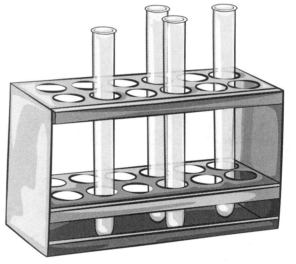

test tube rack

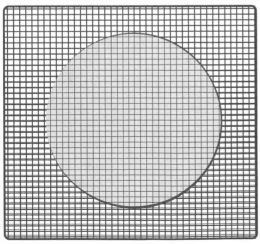

wire gauze

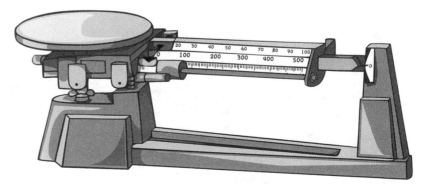

triple-beam balance

APPENDIX C
Laboratory Techniques

USING MECHANICAL SCALES

The masses of substances can be determined in the laboratory with the use of a mechanical scale. Several kinds of mechanical scales or balances are common, but all of them operate on the same principles. To use a mechanical balance properly, follow the steps given below.

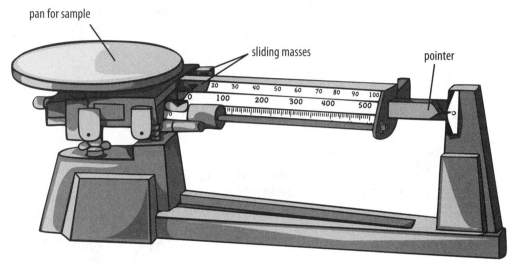

Figure 1 Triple-beam balance

1. Place the balance on a smooth, level surface.

2. Keep the balance pan(s) clean and dry. Never put chemicals directly on the metal surface of the pan(s). Place materials on a sheet of filter paper, on a watch glass, or in a beaker.

3. Check the rest point of the empty balance. To do this, remove all weight from the pans and slide all movable masses to their zero positions. If the balance beam swings back and forth, note the central point of the swing. You do not have to wait until the beam stops swinging completely. If the central point lies more than two divisions from the marked zero point, have your teacher adjust the balance. *Do not adjust the balance yourself!*

4. Place the substance of the mass you are trying to find on the pan and adjust the sliding masses. Move the largest masses first, and then make final adjustments with the smaller masses. The sum of all the readings is the mass of the object (Figure 2). Watch your significant digits!

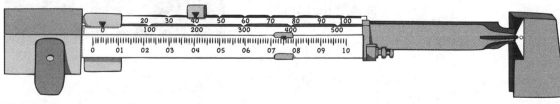

Figure 2 The mass of this sample would be read as 47.51 g.

Figure 3 An electronic scale

USING AN ELECTRONIC SCALE

Electronic scales are generally faster and easier to use than their mechanical counterparts. To use an electronic scale or balance properly, follow the instructions given below.

1. Place the balance on a smooth, level surface.

2. Keep the balance pan(s) clean and dry. Never put chemicals directly on the metal surface of the pan(s). Place materials on a sheet of filter paper, on a watch glass, or in a beaker.

3. Turn the balance on. Place the container or weighing paper that will hold the substance of the mass you are trying to find and make sure that there is a reading of 0 by pushing the "tare" button.

4. Place the substance of the mass you are trying to find on the paper or in the container. Add the desired substance until you have reached the appropriate weight. Watch your significant digits!

USING A LABORATORY BURNER

Laboratory burners are the most common source of heat in chemistry laboratories. They are popular because they give a hot flame and burn clean, readily available natural gas or butane. Laboratory burners work well because they mix gas with the correct amount of air to produce the most heat. If air is not mixed with the gas before it burns, not all the gas will burn, and the flame will not be as hot. If too much air is mixed with the gas, the air will "snuff out" the flame.

Take your laboratory burner apart and then reassemble it, identifying each part as you do. If the burner doesn't have its own gas supply, connect it to the desk gas line with a rubber hose. Open the main gas valve, and light the burner with a match or flint. Adjustments to the flame should be made from the gas and air valves (see Figure 4). If the burner lights but the flame immediately goes out, try increasing the gas flow at the gas valve. A yellow flame signifies that insufficient air is mixing with the gas. A flame that makes a noise like a roaring wind means that too much air is entering the barrel. This extra air may cool the flame or extinguish it entirely.

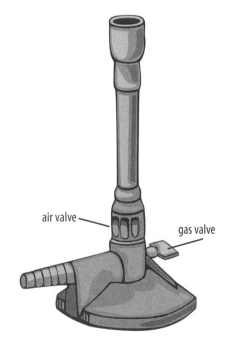

air valve

gas valve

Figure 4 Laboratory burner

To get the best flame possible, rotate the barrel until the flame is entirely blue and two distinct zones appear. Place objects to be heated at the tip of the inner blue zone for quick heating.

Sometimes the flame strikes back; that is, it enters the barrel and comes out the bottom. If this happens, do not panic. Turn off the gas supply and readjust the burner so that less air enters the barrel.

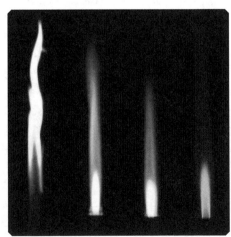

Figure 5 From left to right, this photo shows a flame with an air valve fully closed, mostly closed, partially open, and fully open. The last flame is properly adjusted, showing several cones of flame.

HANDLING LIQUIDS

Proper technique for handling liquids is essential if you are to remain safe, keep reagents pure, and obtain accurate measurements. For increased safety, do not splash or spatter liquids when pouring. Pour them slowly down the insides of test tubes and beakers. If anything is spilled, wipe it up quickly. To keep liquids from running down the outside of the container from which you are pouring, pour the liquid down a stirring rod (see Figure 11 on the next page).

In order to keep the liquid chemicals pure, keep stirring rods out of the stock supply. Do not let the stoppers and lids become contaminated while you are pouring. Instead, hold the stopper between your fingers. If you must put a lid down, keep the inside surface from touching the surface of the table (Figure 6).

wrong right   wrong right

Figure 6 Don't let the part of a lid that touches a chemical also touch your lab bench.

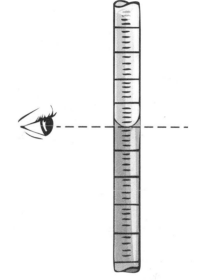

Figure 7 Read the level of a liquid at the bottom of the meniscus.

You can make accurate measurements of liquids in burets, graduated cylinders, and volumetric flasks. You should measure volumes in these pieces of glassware unless you need only a rough approximation of volume. When reading the level of a liquid, look at the bottom of the meniscus (curved surface) along a horizontal line of sight (Figure 7).

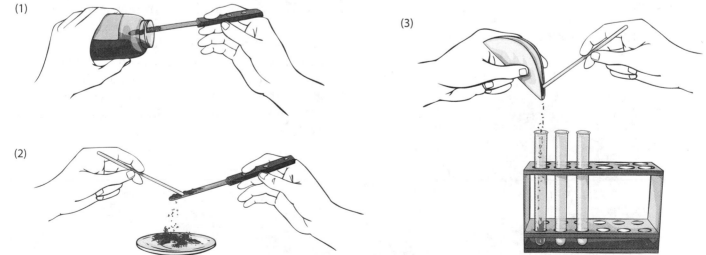

(1)

(2)

(3)

Figure 8 To measure out solids, (1) scoop out a little of the sample. (2) Gently tap the spatula until the desired amount falls off onto the weighing paper. (3) Cup the paper to pour the powdered solid into a test tube.

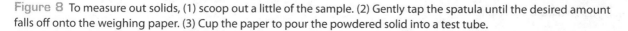

Figure 9 How to properly insert a thermometer into a rubber stopper

USING A THERMOMETER

Select a thermometer that has the proper temperature range for the experiment that you will be doing. Support the thermometer in a one-hole rubber stopper when it is necessary to contain the substance whose temperature the thermometer is measuring. To avoid breaking the thermometer and cutting your hand while inserting the thermometer into the stopper, lubricate the thermometer and the stopper hole with soap or glycerol. Then protect your hands with paper towels. Hold the themometer near the stopper and gently twist it into the hole (Figure 9). If you have to use a great amount of force, ask your teacher to enlarge the hole.

Position the thermometer bulb just above the bottom of the container. If the bulb touches the container, your readings will be inaccurate. If a thermometer breaks, alert your teacher and do not touch the inner contents. Some thermometers contain mercury. Spilled mercury may look fascinating, but it is toxic and can be absorbed through the skin.

SEPARATING LIQUIDS AND SOLIDS

Several experiments require that you separate a solid from a liquid. The most common method of separation—filtering—involves passing the solution through a fine sieve, such as filter paper. The paper allows the liquid and dissolved particles to pass through but catches undissolved particles.

The filter paper must be folded to fit the funnel. Fold it in half and then fold it again at an angle slightly less than 90° to the first fold. Tear off the corner of the last fold as shown in the red circle in Figure 10 to seal the corner. Open the paper to form a cone; half of the cone should have three layers of paper, and the other half should have one layer. Place the cone in a funnel and wet the paper with a few drops of distilled water to hold it in place. Seal the edge of the paper against the edge of the funnel so that none of the solution can go down the spout without going through the paper.

Decanting is a quick method that is often acceptable for separating a liquid from a solid. To decant, allow the solid to settle and then gently pour the liquid off the top of the residue. Avoid causing turbulence that could mix the solid with the liquid. Sometimes the solid residue left in the container is rinsed off with distilled water and decanted a second time to make sure that all the liquid is separated from the precipitate.

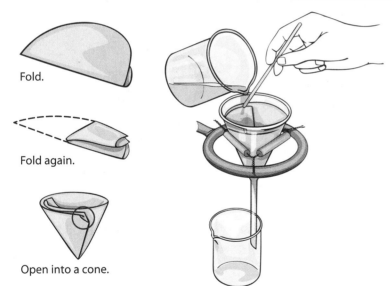

Fold.

Fold again.

Open into a cone.

Figure 10 Folding a piece of filter paper to be used in an apparatus for filtration

Figure 11 Decanting a liquid from a precipitate

APPENDIX D
Graphing Techniques

CONSTRUCTING GRAPHS

When data is recorded in tables, it is difficult to see the relationship that exists between sets of numbers. To make trends and patterns easier to see, you will often put your data on a graph.

In experiments that search for a cause-effect relationship between two variables, you will cause one variable (the independent variable) to change and observe the effect on the second (the dependent variable). If you were to investigate how the solubility of NH_4Cl changes with temperature, temperature would be the independent variable, and solubility would be the dependent variable. Traditionally, the independent variable is plotted on the x-axis of the graph, and the dependent variable is plotted on the y-axis.

As you construct your graph, choose an appropriate scale. Do not make the graph so small that the data cannot be clearly seen or so large that the graph will not fit on a single sheet of paper. Pick a scale that will conveniently include the entire range of each variable. Keep in mind that the scales on each axis do not have to be the same. For instance, the scale on the x-axis might be 5 °C for every division, while the scale on the y-axis could be 2 g for every line. Your scale should be easy to subdivide. Subdivisions of 1, 2, 5, and 10 are the most convenient.

Once you have decided which variable will be plotted on which axis and the scales that will be used, neatly label the name of each quantity and the numbers on each axis. The title of the graph should be printed at the top of the graph. If more than one line will be sketched on the same graph, include a legend that identifies each line. Plot each of your data points by making small dots. Follow the specific lab guidelines for the proper way to handle these data points. You will usually draw a smooth line through the data points. Figure 1 illustrates these techniques.

Table 1 Observed Solubilities of NH_4Cl	
Temperature (°C)	Solubility (g/100 mL H_2O)
10	33
20	37
30	41
40	45
50	50
60	56

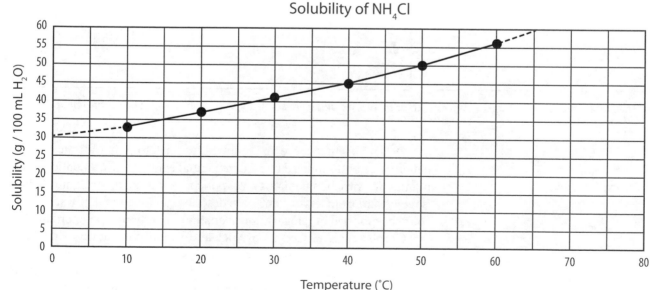

Figure 1 Solubility of NH_4Cl. Notice how all the points are connected.

In some cases, you will want to draw a straight line even though your data points do not fall precisely in a line. If this occurs, draw a line that shows the general relationship. Be sure to make the line go through the average values of the plotted points. In Figure 2, line A is incorrect because it lies above the cluster of points near the bottom of the graph and below the cluster of points at the top. Line B shows the correct method of fitting a straight line to a series of points.

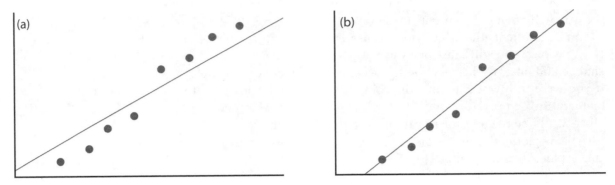

Figure 2 (a) Incorrect method of fitting a straight line to a series of points; (b) correct method of fitting a straight line to a series of points

INTERPRETING GRAPHS

The shape of a graphed line tells much about the relationship between the variables. When data appears to be arranged in a straight line, the x and y variables are related in a way that can be expressed in a linear equation. If this line goes through the origin, the linear equation will express the x variable as a multiple of the y variable. A positive slope means that the x variable increases with the y variable; a negative slope indicates that the x variable decreases as the y variable increases.

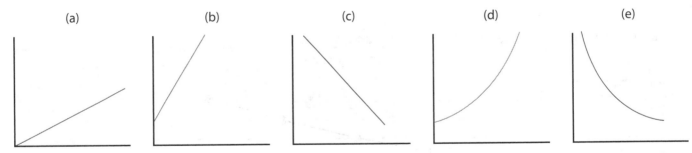
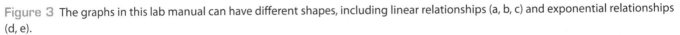

Figure 3 The graphs in this lab manual can have different shapes, including linear relationships (a, b, c) and exponential relationships (d, e).

Data points that curve up (or down) from left to right indicate that the data may be best modeled by an exponential equation. The equation relating the two variables contains an exponent. A curved or straight line that is downward from left to right often describes an inverse relationship. This could be modeled by a logarithmic equation or perhaps a polynomial.

Graphs can be used to predict additional data points that have not been experimentally determined. Assuming that points between verified data points are correct because they fall on the graphed line is called *interpolation*. From the graph of NH_4Cl solubilities (Figure 1), it is reasonable to assume that 43 g of NH_4Cl would dissolve at 35 °C. Extending the graphed line past the verified data points in either direction is called *extrapolation*. The graph of NH_4Cl solubilities indicates that 59 g would dissolve at 65 °C. This extrapolation is reasonable, but it may not be totally accurate.

APPENDIX E
Questing with the LabQuest

Making models is one of the most important things that scientists do. Models can be physical objects, but most are either mathematical equations or visual representations of data. For example, if a scientist wishes to model human growth from birth to adulthood, he would probably graph height versus age (Figure 1). Visual models are especially useful because we are usually much better at interpreting pictures than tables of numbers.

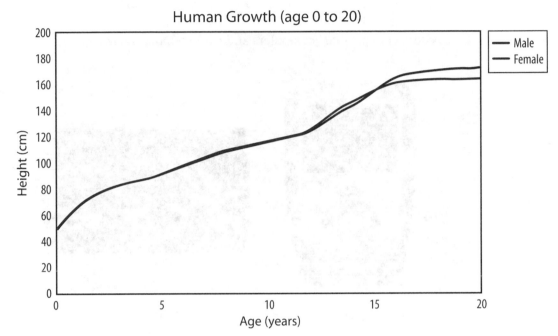

Figure 1 Models are often visual representations of data.

To make models, scientists need *data*, which is usually numbers. Most data comes from *instruments*, devices that measure physical phenomena, turning them into numbers that represent the quantity being measured. But instruments can be expensive, and most measure only one particular phenomenon. This is the reason that many high-school lab activities either don't require students to collect large quantities of data or just give them an existing set of data. In most cases, it's just not practical or affordable to have the students gather their own data.

And then there's a second problem: building anything other than a simple model takes a lot of time and skill. Imagine graphing 500 data points by hand! While graphing software could make the task easier, you still would have to type in the raw data by hand. What's the solution?

PROBEWARE TO THE RESCUE!
In the early 1990s, several companies began to sell educational-grade lab sensors that connected to a personal computer, turning it into a powerful and flexible instrument. Using these systems, students could gather large data sets in many different areas of science including earth science, biology, chemistry, and physics. Modeling was easy too, since the data was already in the computer.

By the mid-2000s the technology had matured and had become affordable and portable. Instead of connecting to a personal computer, the sensors now connect to a small handheld electronic device that includes built-in modeling software. This portability makes it possible to go out into the field and collect data. We call this kind of technology *probeware*. Sensors plug into a compact but powerful handheld device known as the *Vernier LabQuest*.

At the time of this writing, Vernier offers two versions of the device: the original LabQuest and the LabQuest 2 (Figure 2). Both have similar capabilities, although the LabQuest 2 has a few extra features such as a larger screen and built-in wireless networking. Both have rechargeable batteries, powerful modeling software, and the ability to connect to personal computers and USB memory devices.

Figure 2 Original LabQuest® (left) and LabQuest® 2 (right)

LABQUEST HARDWARE OVERVIEW

This appendix provides a basic tutorial for using either the original LabQuest or the LabQuest 2. All the pictures and screen images are from the LabQuest 2, but the original LabQuest is similar. We're going to begin by looking over the outside of the device (the hardware). If you need more detail, you should consult the product documentation, which is available on the LabQuest CD as well as on Vernier's website (www.vernier.com).

Power Button

Turn on the LabQuest by pressing the power button briefly (Figure 3). If the device is completely powered down, it will require a little over a minute to start up. If the device is sleeping, however, it will wake up and be ready to go in just a few seconds.

To put the LabQuest to sleep, press the power button briefly. If you have unsaved experiment data, the LabQuest will give you a choice to save the data or discard it before going to sleep. Putting the unit to sleep extends battery life, while allowing you to power up quickly when needed. *Remember, however, that a sleeping LabQuest is still draining its battery and will eventually run out of power!*

Figure 3 LabQuest 2 top view

To power down the LabQuest completely, press and hold the power button until the shutdown screen appears. When the screen goes dark, the unit is completely off. If you're not going to use a LabQuest for a long period of time, it's better to power it down completely to conserve the battery charge.

Power Connector

Keep your LabQuest charged so that you never miss an experiment! Plug the wall power adapter into the power connector when you're not using your LabQuest. If your lab has a Vernier charging station, just drop the unit into one of the charging pockets so that the docking port engages (see Figure 4).

Figure 4 LabQuest 2 right view

Sensor Ports

Most of the LabQuest sensors plug into the *regular sensor ports* (Figure 5), labeled **CH 1** through **CH 3** (the original LabQuest also has a **CH 4**). A few special sensors plug into the *digital ports*, labeled **DIG 1** and **DIG 2** (see Figure 3).

Recent model sensors automatically identify themselves when you plug them in, so you'll be ready to collect data almost instantly. Older sensors require a special adapter and must be manually identified before they can be used. We'll cover this procedure later.

Figure 5 LabQuest 2 left view

USB Memory Port

While the LabQuest has a fairly large internal memory, it's often convenient to store your experiment data on an external USB memory device so that you can take it home or transfer it to modeling software on a personal computer. Plug your memory device into a USB memory port (see Figure 5) and you're ready to go. We'll discuss how to transfer data to a USB memory device later in this appendix.

USB Computer Port

Sometimes it's useful to connect the LabQuest directly to a personal computer. You can connect a USB cable (provided with each unit) between the LabQuest's USB computer port (see Figure 4) and an available USB port on your computer. The personal computer's modeling software can then directly control the LabQuest and access its data.

Physical Buttons

While you'll interact with the LabQuest mostly through its touchscreen, it does have one physical button that is especially useful: **Collect** (Figure 6). Pressing the **Collect** button tells the LabQuest to start collecting data. A second press halts data collection. You can also control data collection from the touchscreen, but a physical button is very handy.

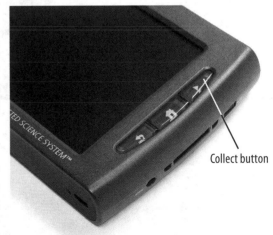

Figure 6 Collect button

LABQUEST SOFTWARE OVERVIEW

The LabQuest's built-in software has two main purposes: *data collection* and *modeling*. Normally, you collect data first and then use the modeling software to display, analyze, and draw conclusions from it. This section summarizes the major parts of the software.

Since the LabQuest has a touchscreen, almost everything is done by *taps*—touching specific parts of the screen with the stylus or your finger. The software has five main *modes*, which are selected by tapping the tabs at the top of the screen.

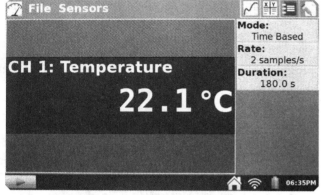

Figure 7   Meter mode

Meter Mode

The LabQuest's *meter mode* (Figure 7) is useful if you have one or more sensors plugged into the sensor ports. This screen provides a live display of the data coming from the sensors (temperature in this example). Select meter mode if you wish to use the LabQuest like a regular lab instrument to take quick measurements without saving the data.

Graph Mode

When you press the **Collect** button, the LabQuest starts gathering data from its sensors and storing it in memory. It displays this data in *graph mode* (Figure 8) as it's being collected, as well as after collection ends. The **Analyze** menu includes numerous tools that you can use to model and manipulate the data.

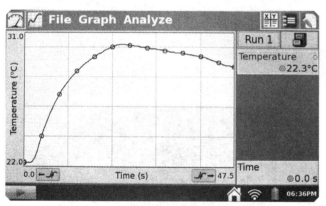

Figure 8   Graph mode

Table Mode

After data collection, if you wish to examine your raw data in number form, tap the *table mode* tab (Figure 9).

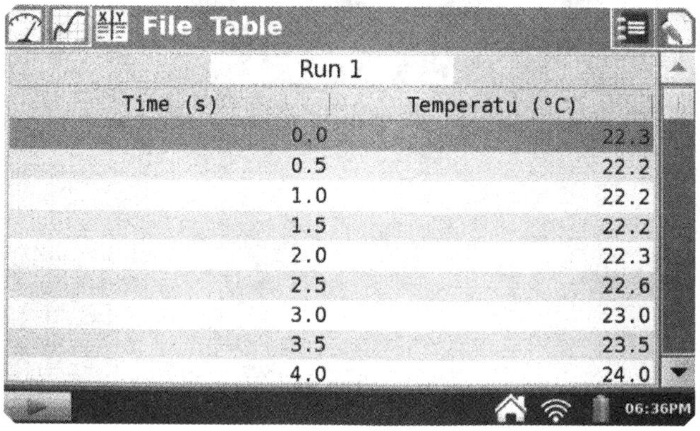

Lab Instructions Mode

The *lab instructions mode* tab is useful if you download a pre-created lab from Vernier, or if your teacher creates a lab for you. Tapping this tab displays the probes and the guidelines or procedure for the lab. None of the labs in this manual uses this tab.

Notes Mode

Good scientists keep notes about their experiments. The LabQuest allows you to enter lab notes and store them along with your data. Simply tap the *notes mode* tab and create your notes by tapping on the miniature keyboard (Figure 10). When you save your experiment, your notes will also be saved.

Figure 9   Table mode

This is a lab note!

Figure 10   Notes mode

STEP-BY-STEP EXPERIMENT

There's no better way to learn how something works than to use it. So let's outline a simple experiment with the LabQuest to help you become familiar with its major features and tools. The LabQuest-based experiments in this manual will then make more sense when you do them.

For our example, we're going to use the Vernier Stainless Steel Temperature Probe to model how a cup of coffee cools over a period of 10 minutes. We'll collect data (temperature), graph it, examine specific parts of the graph, and then use some of the analysis tools. We'll also save our data to the LabQuest's internal memory and to a USB memory device.

Setup

❶ Turn on the LabQuest by pressing the power button. Once it's up and running, connect the temperature probe to CH 1. If you're in meter mode (first tab), you should see the current temperature displayed.

Next, we have to decide on the time period that we wish to collect data and the number of samples that we should collect per second. As a general rule, if your subject of study changes quickly (perhaps several times per second or more), you'll need to collect many samples per second, perhaps several hundred or even several thousand; if more slowly, one sample per second might be enough. Phenomena that change very slowly might need to be sampled just once per minute. Every experiment is different.

❷ For this experiment, we'll collect one temperature sample per second (1 sample/s) for a period of 10 minutes (600 s). To set these two values, tap the meter mode tab and then tap the **Rate** box to the right of the meter display. This will bring up a screen where you can adjust the data collection time values (Figure 11).

❸ Tap the **Duration** (or **Length**) box and enter **600**. Confirm that the unit next to the **Duration** (or **Length**) box is **s** (seconds). If it's not, tap the down arrow next to the unit box and set the unit to **s**. Verify that the **Rate** box is set to **1**. Tap **OK**.

Data Collection

❶ Press the **Collect** button (or tap the **Collect** button located in the lower-left corner of the screen). The LabQuest will change to graph mode and start gathering data.

❷ Place the temperature probe in the cup of hot coffee. Watch the graph. You'll see it changing as the LabQuest collects each sample.

❸ Since this particular experiment is timed (for 10 minutes), you can just sit back and watch the data come in. However, if something goes wrong, you can always halt the data collection by pressing the **Collect** button again.

❹ When data collection is complete, the LabQuest will stop collecting data and remain in the graph mode. The graph that you see is now a complete model of what you were measuring (Figure 12).

Samples

In electronic data collection, each individual measurement is called a sample. It's like a snapshot of the phenomenon that's being measured. The more samples (measurements) per second that you collect, the more detailed the picture of the phenomenon becomes. But you never want to overdo it, or you could wind up with more data than you really need.

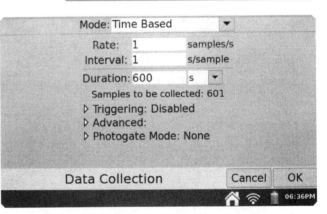

Figure 11 Setting the data collection time information

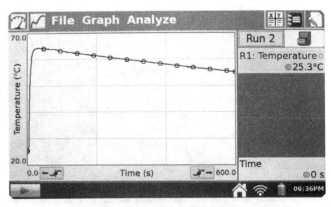

Figure 12 A model of a cooling cup of coffee

Saving Your Data

It's always a smart idea to save your data right away. Generally, you will save it to the LabQuest's internal memory. Later, when you're finished with the experiment, you can save it to a USB memory device to take it with you or to transfer it to a personal computer for further study.

❶ On any mode tab, tap **File** and then **Save**. By default, the filename is **untitled**. Tap it and type a descriptive filename on the miniature keyboard. Tap the Save button, located in the lower-right corner of the screen, to save the data in the LabQuest's memory.

❷ To save your data to a USB memory device, plug the memory device into the LabQuest's USB memory port. Wait several seconds for the LabQuest to activate it.

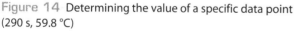
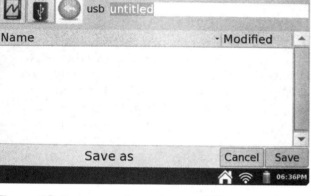

Figure 13 Saving experiment data to a USB memory device

❸ On any mode tab, tap **File** and then **Save**. Select the USB memory device by tapping the USB icon in the upper-left corner of the screen (Figure 13).

❹ By default, the filename is **untitled**. Tap it and type a descriptive filename on the miniature keyboard that appears. Tap the **Save** button, located in the lower-right corner of the screen, to save the data to the USB memory device. When the operation finishes, you may remove the USB memory device.

Analyzing the Model

The LabQuest has many different tools to help you analyze your model. Some of them are fairly complicated, while others are quite simple. Let's examine several to get an idea of what your LabQuest can do.

❶ It's often helpful to know the value of a particular point on the graph. To determine a given location's value, just tap the graph with the stylus at the desired location. The **Time** box in the lower-right corner of the screen will show the x value, while the box near the upper-right corner (**Temperature** in this case) will show the y value (Figure 14).

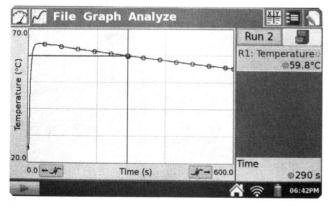

Figure 14 Determining the value of a specific data point (290 s, 59.8 °C)

❷ Sometimes, you need to "zoom in" on a specific part of the graph so that you can examine it more closely. To do this, tap and drag on the graph to highlight the desired section (Figure 15). Then tap **Graph** and **Zoom In**. To zoom back out, tap **Graph** and **Zoom Out**.

❸ In some situations, you need to know the average value of a part of the graph or its maximum/minimum values. To determine these, tap and drag to highlight the part of the graph that you wish to analyze (see Figure 15).

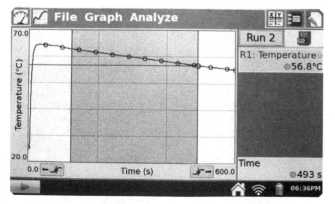

Figure 15 Selecting a specific section of the graph

❹ Next, tap **Analyze** and **Statistics**. Finally, tap the data name (**Temperature** in this case). A statistics box will appear to the right of the model (Figure 16). The **min** and **max** rows show the largest and smallest values within the selected range of data, while the **mean** row shows the average value.

File Management

❶ To open a previous experiment, tap **File** (available on each tab) and then **Open**. Locate the filename, tap it, and then tap the **Open** button, located in the lower-right corner of the screen (Figure 17). If your file is on a USB memory device, you'll need to tap the USB icon in the upper-left corner of the screen to switch from the internal memory to the memory device. You can then select your file and tap the **Open** button.

❷ To keep clutter down, you should delete old experiment files, especially if you've already moved them onto a USB memory device. Erase unneeded files by tapping **File** and then **Delete**. Locate the file, tap it, and then tap the **Delete** button, located in the lower-right corner of the screen.

SENSORS

Sensors with Switches

Some sensors are designed to handle more than one measurement range. For example, the Dual-Range Force Sensor measures forces between ±10 N (~2.25 lb) in 0.01 N (~0.04 oz) increments or ±50 N (~11.2 lb) in 0.05 N (~0.18 oz) increments. Before you can use the sensor, you must decide which range to use and select it by flipping a switch (Figure 18).

Whenever possible, pick a range that's as close as possible to the expected measurement values. You will get better results if you follow these guidelines. For example, if you were using the force sensor to measure a force that was never going to be greater than 2 N, it makes sense to use the ±10 N range rather than the ±50 N.

Zeroing Sensors

Some sensors, especially those that measure force, need to be "zeroed" before they can be used. This is due to the fact that their internal mechanisms always have small forces affecting them to some degree. If you don't zero the sensor, these internal force values will be added to what you're measuring, reducing the measurement's accuracy.

You can tell if you need to zero a sensor of this type by connecting it to the LabQuest and going to the meter mode tab. If the display shows a nonzero value, the sensor should be zeroed before you expose it to any outside influence. For example, a force sensor should have nothing attached to its hook. The zeroing procedure is as follows:

❶ Confirm that the sensor isn't connected to anything that would influence it. For example, a force sensor should have nothing attached to it that would be exerting a force.

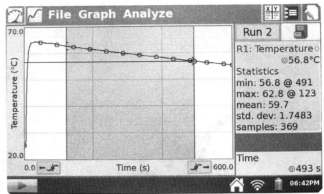

Figure 16 Displaying model statistics

Figure 17 Opening an experiment file

Figure 18 A sensor with a range selector switch

Figure 19 Older sensor connector (top) and cable adapter (bottom)

❷ Tap **Sensors** and then **Zero**. Finally, tap the name of the sensor that you wish to zero. The display should change to a value close to 0. Be aware, however, that it may not go exactly to 0.

Using Older Sensors

Vernier has been making sensors for a long time, so it's possible that you may run into an older model sensor. Most of these will work just fine with the LabQuest, but you'll need to take some extra steps before you can start collecting data.

If the sensor has a large round connector (Figure 19, top) instead of the usual flat connector, you'll need to use an adapter (Figure 19, bottom) to connect it to the LabQuest. Older sensors don't automatically identify themselves to the LabQuest when you plug them in, so you'll need to perform the following steps:

❶ Tap the meter mode tab and then tap **Sensors**. Tap Sensor Setup. Tap the port number (**CH 1**, **CH 2**, **CH 3**, **DIG 1**, or **DIG 2**) that the sensor is connected to (Figure 20).

❷ Scroll through the list until you find your sensor. Tap it and then tap **OK**.

❸ If you have additional sensors connected, repeat steps ❶ and ❷ until you've identified all sensors. Tap **OK** when you're finished. You're now ready to go!

CH 1	No Sensor
CH 2	No Sensor
CH 3	No Sensor
DIG 1	No Sensor
DIG 2	No Sensor

☐ GPS   ☐ Microphone
☐ Accelerometer (X)   ☐ Accelerometer (Y)
☐ Accelerometer (Z)   ☐ Light Sensor
☐ Temperature

Sensor Setup   Cancel   OK

Figure 20 Manually selecting an older sensor

LET THE QUEST BEGIN!

We hope that, by now, you're getting pretty eager to put your LabQuest to work. It's an amazing and versatile tool that allows you to gather data quickly and easily. Best of all, it encourages you to focus on what you can learn from your data rather than the mechanics of gathering and modeling it.

After you've done a few of the LabQuest-based labs in this manual, start thinking about other inquiries where the LabQuest might be helpful. Be curious and think "outside the box." Create your own experiments rather than just doing the ones assigned in class. Don't forget science fair projects either! Real data can transform an average project into an extraordinary one. If your school's biology classroom has a nano reef aquarium, consider monitoring temperature, dissolved oxygen, or nitrate levels. An earth science field trip to study eutrophication (excessive algae growth) in a local lake is a good opportunity to monitor dissolved ammonia in the water. Study exercise in your health class by monitoring heart rate, blood pressure, and respiration rate. Use a carbon dioxide sensor and an oxygen sensor to see photosynthesis at work. Force, pressure, temperature, and acceleration sensors are great tools when you're studying physics. Just think what Galileo could have done with a Vernier motion sensor—better yet, imagine what you can do with one!

So get out there, gather some data, and build a model. That's what science is all about!

APPENDIX F
Periodic Table of the Elements

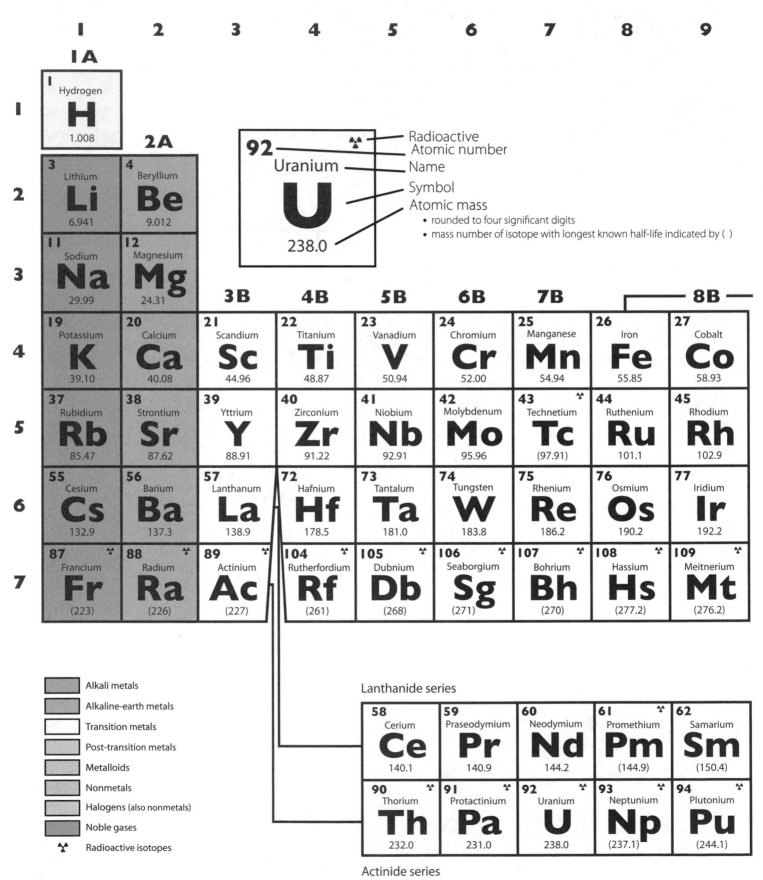

	1	2	3	4	5	6	7	8	9
	1A								

Key:
92 — Atomic number
Radioactive
Uranium — Name
U — Symbol
238.0 — Atomic mass
• rounded to four significant digits
• mass number of isotope with longest known half-life indicated by ( )

Period 1
1 Hydrogen **H** 1.008

Group 2A

Period 2
3 Lithium **Li** 6.941
4 Beryllium **Be** 9.012

Period 3
11 Sodium **Na** 29.99
12 Magnesium **Mg** 24.31

3B 4B 5B 6B 7B 8B

Period 4
19 Potassium **K** 39.10
20 Calcium **Ca** 40.08
21 Scandium **Sc** 44.96
22 Titanium **Ti** 48.87
23 Vanadium **V** 50.94
24 Chromium **Cr** 52.00
25 Manganese **Mn** 54.94
26 Iron **Fe** 55.85
27 Cobalt **Co** 58.93

Period 5
37 Rubidium **Rb** 85.47
38 Strontium **Sr** 87.62
39 Yttrium **Y** 88.91
40 Zirconium **Zr** 91.22
41 Niobium **Nb** 92.91
42 Molybdenum **Mo** 95.96
43 Technetium **Tc** (97.91)
44 Ruthenium **Ru** 101.1
45 Rhodium **Rh** 102.9

Period 6
55 Cesium **Cs** 132.9
56 Barium **Ba** 137.3
57 Lanthanum **La** 138.9
72 Hafnium **Hf** 178.5
73 Tantalum **Ta** 181.0
74 Tungsten **W** 183.8
75 Rhenium **Re** 186.2
76 Osmium **Os** 190.2
77 Iridium **Ir** 192.2

Period 7
87 Francium **Fr** (223)
88 Radium **Ra** (226)
89 Actinium **Ac** (227)
104 Rutherfordium **Rf** (261)
105 Dubnium **Db** (268)
106 Seaborgium **Sg** (271)
107 Bohrium **Bh** (270)
108 Hassium **Hs** (277.2)
109 Meitnerium **Mt** (276.2)

Legend:
- Alkali metals
- Alkaline-earth metals
- Transition metals
- Post-transition metals
- Metalloids
- Nonmetals
- Halogens (also nonmetals)
- Noble gases
- Radioactive isotopes

Lanthanide series
58 Cerium **Ce** 140.1
59 Praseodymium **Pr** 140.9
60 Neodymium **Nd** 144.2
61 Promethium **Pm** (144.9)
62 Samarium **Sm** (150.4)

Actinide series
90 Thorium **Th** 232.0
91 Protactinium **Pa** 231.0
92 Uranium **U** 238.0
93 Neptunium **Np** (237.1)
94 Plutonium **Pu** (244.1)

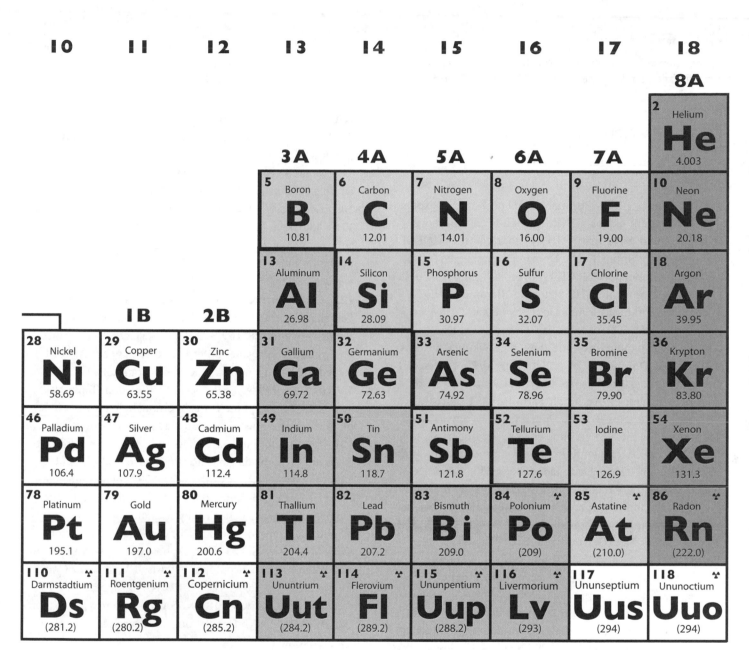

The names given to elements 113, 115, 117 and 118 represent the Latin and Greek names for their arabic numbers.

PHOTO CREDITS

Key: (t) top; (b) bottom; (l) left; (r) right

Cover

Front Science Photo Library-PASIEKA/Brand X Pictures/ Getty Images; **back, spine** © iStockphoto.com/Kerstin Waurick

Front Matter

v © iStockphoto.com/Kali Nine LLC

1 Public Domain; **2** Wavebreak Media/Thinkstock; **8** explosive "GHS-pictogram-explos"/UNECE/Wikimedia Commons/ Public Domain; **8** corrosive "GHS-pictogram-acid"/UNECE/ Wikimedia Commons/Public Domain; **8** carcinogen "GHS-pictogram-silhouete"/UNECE/Wikimedia Commons/Public Domain; **8** flammable "GHS-pictogram-flamme"/UNECE/ Wikimedia Commons/Public Domain; **8** toxic "GHS-pictogram-pollu"/UNECE/Wikimedia Commons/Public Domain; **8** gases "GHS-pictogram-bottle"/UNECE/Wikimedia Commons/Public Domain; **15** Mary Beth Angelo/Photo Researchers/Getty Images; **17** Charles D Winters/Photo Researchers/Getty Images; **19** "Anthropic Farm Units"/Unitfreak/ Wikimedia Commons/Public Domain; **21** Devonyu/iStock/ Thinkstock; **25t** "1796 half dime obverse" by Robert Scot, Image by Lost Dutchman Rare Coins/Wikimedia Commons/ Public Domain; **25b** DrHuckstable/iStock/Thinkstock; **26** Vyacheslav Surov/iStock/Thinkstock; **31** NASA and S. Immler (Swift Team, Goddard Space Flight Center); **35** "Verschiedene LEDs" by Afrank99/Wikimedia Commons/CC BY-SA 2.0; **36** N.A. Sharp, NOAO/NSO/Kitt Peak FTS/AURA/NSF; **39t** Volkan Ertörer/iStock/Thinkstock; **39b** Jeremy Edwards/ iStock/Thinkstock; **43l** "Elementspiral (polyatomic)" by DePiep/Wikimedia Commons/CC BY-SA 3.0; **43r** "Helium atom QM" by Yzmo/Wikimedia Commons/GNU FDL 1.3, CC BY-SA 3.0; **49** "Bulletproof glass window after a burglary attempt" by Raimond Spekking/Wikimedia Commons/ CC BY-SA 3.0; **55l** Angelo Hornak/Alamy; **55r** SangHyun-Paek/iStock/Thinkstock; **58** "Propane-3D-vdW-B" by Ben Mills/Wikimedia Commons/Public Domain; **63** © iStock photo.com/markchentx; **66** © iStockphoto.com/Simon Owler; **69** "Proust Joseph"/Wikimedia Commons/Public Domain;

70 © dgstudio | Dreamstime.com; **76t** "Cobalt(II)-chloride-hexahydrate-sample" by Benjah-bmm27/Wikimedia Commons/Public Domain; **76b** "Cobalt Blue" by FK1954/Wikimedia Commons/Public Domain; **78** "Gas hydrates 1996"/ USGS/Wikimedia Commons/Public Domain; **79** JACOPIN/ BSIP/SuperStock; **83** © iStockphoto.com/magnetcreative; **87** Andy Cross/Denver Post/Getty Images; **90** © Anatoly Tiplyashin | Dreamstime.com; **93** © Christoph Gerigk; **101** Dorling Kindersley/Thinkstock; **103** Andrew Cline/Alamy; **105** Eric Krouse/Shutterstock.com; **107** Sandy Macys/Alamy; **111** © iStockphoto.com/rmnunes; **113t** "Cyclooctasulfur-above-3D-balls" by Benjah-bmm27/Wikimedia Commons/ Public Domain; **113b** © iStockphoto.com/Terry Wilson; **115** © iStockphoto.com/samaro; **116** © iStockphoto.com/oticki; **123** Minden Pictures/SuperStock; **127** "The Siege and Relief of Gibraltar" by John Singleton Copley/Wikimedia Commons/ Public Domain; **128, 169** BJU Photo Services; **133** © iStock photo.com/SeanPavonePhoto; **136** "Circuit board successfully etched" by Filip Dominec/Wikimedia Commons/CC BY-SA 3.0, GNU 1.2; **139** NASA/STScI; **142** TodUdom/Bigstock .com; **145** © iStockphoto.com/PrecisionDigital; **149** © iStock photo.com/gerenme; **151l** © iStockphoto.com/aimintang; **151r** © Donatella Tandelli-Fotolia.com; **152** "Thymolblau" by Yikrazuul/Wikimedia Commons/CC BY-SA 3.0, GNU 1.2; **157** © iStockphoto.com/Olaf Speier; **159** "Phenolphthalein-low-pH" by Benjah-bmm27/Wikimedia Commons/Public Domain; **163** "Volta batteries" by Alessandro Volta [detail]/ Wikimedia Commons/Public Domain; **172** © iStockphoto .com/MTMCOINS; **173** © iStockphoto.com/senorcampesino; **176** "High Performance Rope" by Justsail/Wikimedia Commons/CC BY-SA 3.0, GNU 1.2; **177** NHPA/SuperStock; **180** © iStockphoto.com/egal; **187** NASA/Japan Aerospace Exploration Agency (JAXA); **189** National Nuclear Security Administration/Nevada Site Office

Back Matter

198 "Bunsen burner flame types" by Arthur Jan Fijałkowski/ Wikimedia Commons/CC BY-SA 3.0, GNU 1.2; **204** all, **205** all, **206** all, **207t, b, 208** all, **209** all, **210** all, Don Congdon